SLOWLY, BY THY HAND UNFURLED

HARCOURT, BRACE & WORLD, INC.

NEW YORK

SLOWLY, BY THY HAND UNFURLED

ROMULUS LINNEY

for Laura
some years from now
with love

CONTENTS

I

FORGE

March 24 It is very close today   I am so tired   Well I
will just start   This is the day I started my Journal March 24

25 When I was a little girl Father taught me letters
watching him make them in his Journal a big book
he wrote in every single day how I wish I had that
book now to guide me but it was burned with the
barn twenty years ago   Evie thinks she is well
enough to do things around the house

26   Dr Rudge says Evie can go outside now whenever she wants to   I am so happy to see her up and out of bed again her old self on the porch swing reading her books there   Out there studying herself silly today   Got a letter from the boys Charlie wrote most of it Ed just a little they say they still like the City   Alice died three years ago tomorrow night

27   Have been upstairs to put a carpet down in Evies room   I mean to keep that room nice   I have it fixed up so it will stay pleasant looking and homelike while she is to board at the boarding house this spring term as the walking back and forth will be very bad some of the time   She has a pleasant roommate May Sanford of West Conely   That young Arthur Moore came around today to ask after Evie   I just told him she is in school now

28   Because of Evie I forgot about my Alice sweet Alice gone from her mother three years ago last night in that fit and trembeling   I was cross with Evie who came home today to see Arthur Moore just one day after he had asked about her   How she knew he had been here asking I dont know   Nothing would do but they sit on the porch half the night I was so tired and cross   David said I shouldnt worry so but I didnt listen to him and so forgot about my sweet Alice   Went on out to the Sematary today and told her how sorry I was that I forgot my darling even for one night   It was sunny there today and birds singing   Saw several people I knew

29 Evie has recovered so well   You would think she was a different girl   She slept in her room last night   Said sometimes she will sleep at school sometimes at home depending on Arthur   I came and she was dressing in all the east window sunlight and looked so young and healthy   She kissed me and said she was so happy to be up and about in school again and I ought not to fret myself about Arthur Moore that he is a decent young man   She has grown so beautiful this last year

30 Arthur Moore came this morning to drive Evie to school   She thinks a good deal of him that is plain enough but if he should turn out not to be all he pretends she will have enough sense not to have anything to do with him I know that   Letter from Ed in the City with one of his drawings on the back Some building there   Worked some in the yard David hurt his back rubbed it with linament

31 Went to see Dr Rudge to make sure about Evie he said she was much much improved   She does look that way I have to say so   He didnt know anything about Arthur Moore except he works clerking in the bank   I knew that Journal didnt I   Spent the rest of the morning in town helping David at the store   His back is better and he could wait on people by noon time so I came home It is so lonly here now both boys gone   Evie in school   My sweet Alice gone only three years and already one annivercery forgot about   That is what Time is

April 1   Evie has been home again from school   Says she feels a little homesick   I know thats true she wanted to be home and not because of Arthur Moore neither   I think it seems so odd to have her at school so near and not at home   I miss her so much when we set down to our meals   I said to David tonight when Evie was on the porch waiting what should we do about her   He says yes it will be rather lonly here now but he smiled at the same time I can see he doesnt mind it   After all he has his store works in it all day draws the shades stays there most of the night   I have had a good deal to do today   Calistra was nice to me while she did the wash and sang some of her songs to help my spirit   She is a blessing   I have to make out my list now Evie and May Sanford are coming to-morrow to stay over Sunday

   15   I do not feel very well am so afraid I am going to be sick what should I do   I should so hate to take Evie out of school   Two whole weeks have passed you just cant write in your journal every day can you   I wonder how Father was able to do it there were four or five of those big books when he died all of them burned and lost   I have been so sick Evie had to come home and do the work   David took care of me Calistra helped but there is just too much to do   Evie was out of school again two weeks almost darling girl how good she has been how pleased she was to do the cooking   She made bread for the first time   Carrie Wheaton was married today April 15   I am not very strong but am doing my work   Evie has gone back to school now but comes down almost every day to see how I

am getting along   Arthur Moore drives her in his rig   He waits for her out in front of the white picket gate David painted so white last month
There he stands picking his teeth waiting   Well I had another good letter from my boys today both wrote on the same sheet mailed only four days ago in the City   Things just go too fast these days it gives alarm   Ed drew picture of horse and fire wagon on the back

16 David had to work all night at the store   Evie came to see me but didnt stay very long she went on back to school with Arthur Moore   I was so lonly Calistra came by to get her kerchief she had left here earlier and she stayed with me for a little while and was a blessing   I am so tired and dont want to be sick any more

May 5 Evie has left us my precious child is dead how can I write these terrible words   Evie dead   O my God I cannot have it but I must submit how can I ever say Gods will be done

6 What a day this has been my darling laid away in the parlour all alone the doors closed people coming and going taking their last look of our darling
Only a short time ago she was there in all her strength and beauty now she is dead how can I live but I must be calm for the boys are coming soon

7 The boys came last night   O what a scene Charlie went into spasms when they told him at the station   Did not know anything for several hours We feared he would never come out of it   Sent

7

for the Dr he gave Charlie something to quiet his
nerves   My poor Charlie always so jumpy either
very high or very low never in between   He
is better today but is in a dredful condition the least
word throws him into those spasms   Evie was his
blood sister he loved her so much   Ed feels dred-
fully too but she is not his blood sister and he was
better prepared for the news as he received my letter
saying Evie was back in bed with the migrane dis-
ease in her sweet head and we thought Dr Rudge
was right and she could not live and we would leave
it up to him whether to tell Charlie or not   He
just did not dare tell Charlie then   He only said
to him that Evie was home in bed again the school-
work had been too much for her all at once   This
is Charlies first real grief   He was so young just
a boy really when poor Alice died   We kept it all
from him as much as we could   He was only puzzled by her sickness when she was lying in her room
suffering the torments of her great misfortune and
flight   And of course David had Charlie out of
the house when they brought sweet Alice in from
that terrible slaughterhouse where she almost bled
to death and when Charlie came back the next day
from camping he was just a hungry boy and I gave
him some mince pie and he went on to sleep   But
it is different now poor Charlie   Alice being so
much older and my first husband Edwards child but
Evie his own sister only a year between them his joy
and pleasure now dead in the parlour   Eds great
blow was Alice when she died his blood sister what
a thing that was what a terrible blow to Ed away in
the Army then with nobody to comfort him my poor
boy but now he is able to stand this better   He

drew pictures of all sorts of flowers with a big pen
and stuck them on the wall over her coffin
Flowers in lots of wavy grass that looks like fire
You almost thought sweet darling Evie would get up
to look at them just rise and step out like you get
out of a bathtub they were so pretty and distinktive
looking up there   My brother Henry came on the
three oclock train I was glad to see him and treated
him very nicely and he was very sensible and helpful
to us all   O God only three weeks ago today May
Sanford and Sarah Edson came here and went to
church with my darling she was sick then with the
headache   Now they are all here again with all
the girls from the school dressed in sweet white
dresses and carrying donations of flowers going into
the dark parlour to look at their beloved schoolmate
I told Charlie about Arthur Moore what he had been
up to   Dear Calistra has been here all day doing
whatever she could   Once I walked into the
pantry crying and she came in after me   She
looked so foolish and woeful and she patted my
shoulder dear Calistra   She looked like a big
black sow so heavy with care   She started to cry
saying yes I know I only work for you but you
know how I feel and she asked me if I wanted her to
be a comfort to me   I said you are you are dear
Calistra but not now not right now please dont
think about it now I will be all right and she went
on out of the pantry   I told Charlie how much
strain Evie had been under because of Arthur Moore

8 This terrible day is past   We have laid our darling Evie away in the cold silent grave   Friends
have gone and we are left in all our lonliness can I

ever learn to live without my darling it seems to me my heart is burning up but I must be calm and not distress my poor boys   They have all they can bear without my adding to their grief   Arthur Moore came to the service and tried to stand there by the grave but Charlie pushed him back   When the funeral was over and darling Evie gone forever Charlie took after Arthur Moore with a spade they held him and got it away from him but then Charlie hit Arthur Moore a good one and bloodied his nose until Ed got him under control   Then later Ed started crying and Charlie did for him   How each one is trying to control his feelings each one trying to help the other

9   Went this forenoon where my darling lies   There in that same Semetary with Edward my early husband and with Alice   Another day gone with all its lonliness

10   Have been trying to regulate the house a little bit How dredful it is to see Charlie going from one room to the other   He seems so broken hearted his little sister is gone he did not know how much he loved her until she left him   He has been trying to play Evies favorite hymn on the pianno How The Gates Came Adjar   It was sung at the funeral by Mrs Phiney   Charlie and Evie I remember how when they were children in the back yard playing by the old chickenhouse she would sing that hymn while he would jump rope

11   Have been quite sick today Ed has to go tomorrow how can I let him leave me now Charlie either

12   Ed has gone   So serious and sober all the time
So thin now I worry about that   How hard it was
for him to leave us and go back to the great City
Charlie must go soon

13   It is dredful O my father in Heaven help me or I
shall sink   Friends have called to give us their
sympathy but it does not ease the pain in my heart
how can they know what I feel

14   Today is Sunday the first Sabbath after Evies
funeral   It seemed to me I must go and rap on
the pipe that runs up to her room through the ceiling
for her to come and comb my hair and go to church
with me   Charlie goes about the house looking so
lonly   He cannot speak of Evie with any calmness   We are very anxious about him   He has
got to go back to his business maybe it will be the
best thing for him but so hard for me   Had a
beautiful letter from Reverend Bayley a kind and
understanding man of God but what does he know
Charlie acting so strange   I wish I knew what to
say to him   He is like a prickley pear even now in
this terrible time   Chews his inside lip and stares
and stares at things   He wont listen to anything
I say   David tries to cope with him but nobody
pays David any mind rightly so

15   One week since she was buried can it be yes one
week I have lived without my darling   Letter
from Etta Holibrook

11

16   Another beautiful letter from Reverend Bayley full
of sympathy wrought out with beautiful penmanship
I hope its the last one   Have had many other letters some from Evies schoolmates

17   Charlie must go tomorrow how I dred it we shall be
all alone   But it is best for him to go   Letter
from poor Ed mailed the day after he left what fast
service   He is so lonly and I know he wants to
come back but he made his move to the City and has
his work there at the glass factory that keeps him
busy   Charlie said he isnt making enough money
but then you never know what Charlie means when
he talks about money he doesnt understand what it
is

18   Charlie has gone to the train with his father with
him to see him off   He had to go on the night
train darling boy how hard he tried to control his
feelings how hard he tried to be brave on my account   He would hardly even speak to me afraid
to upset me and suffering within himself rather than
be comforted by his mother   But just before he
left the house he put both hands on my shoulders
and looked at me with tears and misery in his handsome eyes saying O Mother I am sorry if I have
made you unhappy with my moody thoughts   I
said O Charlie hush and kissed him goodbye
Here I am all alone in the house   How ernestly I
prayed just now that this great grief may bring both
my boys to Jesus Ch bless them heavenly father and
keep   O I am so tired and sick and lonly I hardly
know what I am saying   Sometimes I talk out
loud and that scares me but though my actions seem

strange my grief is great and God will not condem
a woman who speaks out loud when no one is here

19   O what a barren day this has been   No one can
tell what it is   How I miss my precious child my
darling Evie my babe my pride my great joy O with
what anguish I saw the shadow of death pass over
that beautiful face   I cannot forget it it is en-
gravind on my heart and soul forever   I suppose
I ought not to think of it so much   God help me
to remember that it is He who has taken my jewel
from me   I must not forget he has left me my
husband dear David out pitching horseshoes the day
after the funeral how can he do it but he is a man
and I must be glad he is left to me because he has
been very kind these last days in this great sorrow
And I still have my precious boys but they are in the
City   Still they are mine   And so many kind
friends sympathizing with me gathering around me
in this time of bereavement   I must give thanks
give thanks

20   Have been working in the yard today weeding
The garden will be all right this year I think
Have been taking care of some of dear Evies things
Took up the carpet in her room only laid down just
such a little while before for her pleasure and comfort   Have had a letter from Jane Simmons
one from May Sanford

21   Sabbath again   Have been to church   No Evie
to sit with me and sing with me   How hard it is
I wish I could control my feelings more in church I
think I will have to stay away this will not do to

set and cry but I cannot help it   Reverend Bayley said so many things about being young and innocent and what the worldly will do to that and talked so much about it   Then they sang Only A Rose Will Do which was also sung at the funeral I think   I suppose they mean well or think they do but it seemed to me I would faint or do something dredful   They kept on and on and wouldnt stop

same day   Mavis Grant has just now been to the house   O avenging God of righteousness and justice now I see why good Reverend Bayley talked so about youth and innocence and why they were all so aware of me why I was stared at so   I thought it was just me sensitive in my sorrow but Mavis Grant just told me that he was in the church   He is come back here how can he dare to show his face Dr Craig the man who butchered my sweet Alice   Mavis says he is telling people he means to take up his practice again We will see about that

22   I have been everywhere today seen everybody but it is no use   Dr Rudge says there is nothing he can do about it   Reverend Bayley says there is nothing he can do either and the Sherrif who is not a intelligent man says the same   He has been pardoned and let out and thats all there is to it right now   But they say they will all watch him like hawks   O God how can you see him walk the streets that man who plunged his knife and filthy dirty hands into the womb of my sweet Alice who delivered her of child and life in a pool of red precious blood so that I was screaming for three months after how can you how can you

same day   I have made myself some tea and drunk it   Dr
Craig is pardoned and out of prison   There is
nothing I can do about that   I must wait upon
the Lord who will claim his vengeance   Mavis
told me Dr Craigs big black beard is white in places
now and his hands shake and when he talks he clears
his throat over and over again and wont look anybody in the eye   They only kept him in prison
three years and yet he killed my child but I will
wait on you just God vengeance is yours upon William Craig and I will wait to see it come about and
do my work   David helps me and is kind to me
I do not know what I would do without him but of
course when I talked to him about William Craig
David just nodded and said there was nothing we
can do   He is so kind and such a weakling

23   Have had letters from my dear boys   Dear Ed
how he tries to comfort his mother   He drew a
picture of a girl in a flaming sun with her arms held
up in the air   On great wings angels diving down
to her from heaven above the only thing about it
the girl was naked and her arms were burning up he
made a mistake somewhere poor dear Ed he means
well

24   Have just been doing my work   Have had many
callers   David says he does not see how I can
bear to talk so much about Evie and Alice too now
because that William Craig has come back to town
but I love to tell all about my darlings and I know
the wrath of God will descend   O Alice and my
beautiful Evie   At least he cannot practice medicine any more that was all a lie they have taken

away his liscence for good and so there is no way he can treat anybody else and kill anybody else too late for me Alice dead at his hands   Nobody knows what he will do now   They say he is trying to sell his old house   Mavis Grant says no one will buy it from him because of Alice   Maybe he will have to be a vetinary and treat with dogs and cats even that is too good for him

25   Have gathered all the spring flowers I could in my wicker basket and carried them to the Semetary to decorate the Soldiers and my darling Evies grave Alices too   Evie did it for me last year brought the flowers in her sweet hands and while I stood by so proud she put them on Alice her half sisters grave   Little then did I think she would be sleeping here on the next 25 of May   Everything is very beautiful here   Edwards tombstone I had to have it scraped off but it is still handsome like he was that man of pride and fierce temper except of course it is aged now a little some of the stone turned dark even the scraping didnt help and Evies so new and well carved and Alices nice too   I will do this again soon come here to them and the flowers help so much more than any people can

June 2   I have been many times to the Semetary   David has told me I must not go so often any more people are beginning to worry about me   I said what does that mean and he said well they are just worried about you   I said you mean you are afraid business is falling off at the store people are not coming in there like you think they should just because I take flowers to the graves of my loved ones

16

He said no no no but that was it   David David
David David David

3   Everything is beautiful now the trees the flowers the
grass is so green God with rain and gentle showers
has washed the earth   How I have from child-
hood loved the month of June so did Evie but it
seems to me now that I am looking through a glass
darkly everything is so changed   I cannot enjoy
the beautiful weather my heart aches so O how I try
to think how much our heavenly father has done for
us in giving us all the beautiful works of nature but
I keep thinking how much better he made them than
us   Strange thoughts   I would so like to be
dogwood and tulip and not suffer   Well journal
now you see what happens when a woman writes in
a book and doesnt get her housework done   I
have a lot more to do today and I will start now
praising God however he made us and only hope
I may not be unreasonable in my grief

4   I determined I would go to church today   Even
asked David if he would go with me useless thing to
do   As always he said no   Put on his baggy
browns and went off to idly fish and waste his time
with those Moulton brothers and that filthy Joe
Waggoner who is part Indian   I know how they
spend the Sabbath morning just wallowing around
they dont bring back enough fish to show any purpose in their day they just stick the pole in the
ground and lie about drinking until they cant see
But David has his way of getting home sober at all
times   I have never seen him drunk and he fools
me about it that way and I can say nothing   I

went to church alone I went a little bit late so as not to be sitting there if William Craig came in the door and might sit close to me   Some heads turned about when I came quietly in   Rev Bayley nodded at me just a hair and smiled a beautiful smile just the way when I was a child the dear hand and easy smile of my father welcomed me when I came into a room where he was   So I went in feeling all right and took the first near seat and only when I got settled saw I had seated myself just behind and a little to the left of him William Craig It was a while before I could bring myself to look at him but I did finally   Mavis was so right he has many white hairs his skin is sallow his hands shake now holding the hymnal but they did not shake when they plunged the tearing ripping knife up into the soft flesh of my Alice sweet child no matter what she did my sweet Alice mortally wounded and dying in a pool of her precious blood the spirit leaving in agony that sweet flesh sinful though it might have been when we are young we can not know what lies in store for us Alice   Visiting preacher Mr Putnam spoke   I did not hear much of what he had to say   William Craig only put a dime a thin dime in the collection he must be hard up now   When I got home I sorted out the wash Calistra did for me yesterday   It was all so clean and well done   That wonderful girl   She is a blessing

5   Mrs Nutt came to see me today   She tried to be kind and she meant well I suppose but she is so rich it is hard for her to know what she thinks she has to do   But she must know somewhat how I feel she

has lost a daughter too but she has three left   I
tried to get something out of her about William
Craig but she wouldnt talk   He was her doctor
once I think something or other between them one
time anyhow   She could help him now if she
wanted to but they say she doesnt   So just let him
alone then everybody God will judge   Mrs Nutt
wears glasses cant see too well she slipped going
down my porch steps almost fell   She looked so
flap armed and foolish dropped her pairasol popped
her mouth open and shut in panik   Her skirts
came up and her long bony legs showed   She
staggered about there grabbing the air and almost
got hurt I guess but only ended up just sitting down
plump dropping her bag and two books she had and
her eyeglasses fell off   She was so funny and odd
looking   All that money her cross to bear   It
makes her do things like this come to see me only
because she thinks she is supposed to somehow
Pitiful   All that money her cross to bear I wish I
had some of it journal dont you

6 Mrs Nutt came here again today for goodness sakes
Thank goodness I thought when Mrs Phiney walked
by stopped and joined us on the porch   Mrs
Nutt was not very happy to see her it seemed
Mrs Phiney left in just a minute not very happy
about Mrs Nutt who was cold to her   Mrs Nutt
stayed a solid hour what have I done to deserve that
I finally got rid of her   What does she think I
have to do these days just sit on the porch with
her good glory   Scrubbed the kitchen floor and
cleaned the flues   Calistra will be surprized when
she comes tomorrow   Mrs Nutt said she heard I

19

had a fine girl named Calistra   I said yes I am
envied because of her all right

7 Today Calistras day and I was so happy to see her

8 Nothing happened at all today   I have tried to
become more submissive to God's will   I know
my darling is happy up there Evie in her beautiful
home all through with the trials of this life
David has been away for two days   I am so
lonly I was even glad to see Mrs Nutt when she
stopped by today for a while

9 Today I went with Mrs Nutt Fanny Knap Mrs
Phiney and Mavis Grant to see Mrs Hardy Allens
mother who is failing   Mrs Nutt got tired soon
and we came back here   Calistra stopped work
and made us all some tea and I managed to provide
proper diversion   Dear Calistra made sure I got
my own teacup with the jasmine painted on it a
little different and prettier than the others   But
when Calistra handed Mrs Nutt her cup Mrs Nutt
upset it and spilled tea all over herself   I got up
to help but Mrs Nutt said oh no dont bother Calistra will get me a rag wont you Calistra   Calistra
got a rag and came back in with it for Mrs Nutts
dress   I thought she would never get Mrs Nutt
dried off to that womans satisfaction   She had to
rub and rub with Mrs Nutt saying harder please
Calistra harder thats it   We then drank tea and
finally they left   It is so hot and close today
I feel tired if my darling was only here I could rest
it is so hard not to see her and hear her say did you
have a good time mother

aturdays   I will never forgive Calistra or speak
o her again while we live on this earth

abbath today   In the middle of the service Rev
Bayley talked so sweetly about the joys of this
our life here on earth and how grateful we must be
for them that I cried and cried   I must not do
that again it is shameful but I did   I cried and
said out loud Im afraid right out loud yes yes that
is right yes   Rev Bayley was not upset at all
and several heads turned and smiled at me
William Craig sitting across the ile got the shakes
then had a coffing spell and everybody stared hard
at him   William Craig had to get up and leave
the Church   Charlie caught a bass and David
two fair sized perch yesterday I broiled them today
good fish

I can't get anything out of David about Charlie
Charlie of course wont say anything to me these
days at all and I dont know why   They are
funny the two of them father and son   I dont
know what passes between them at all   And you
know journal isnt it funny the way they do everything opposite of each other well I guess thats natural   David who wont wear any but old clothes
Now I keep them clean for him as I always have
but still he roots himself down in them and lives
in those fishing clothes and baggy old brown things
like a hogs digging down into the mud   Charlie
on the other hand always dressed up in striped
jacket and he has four or five of them those straw
boaters and those white shoes he cleans himself
every morning   This morning he had a band

10   Nothing happened today   Calistra sent word she
is down sick with flue   But she sent me her
younger sister Josie to work for me today and do
the wash   She is a nice girl has the same happy
disposition Calistra has except she doesnt wash so
well   David home tomorrow   He has been to
the City to see the boys what about I dont know
business he said   David is funny about the boys
He has always seemed to like Ed so much better
than Charlie his own son   You would think a
man would not like his wifes son by early marriage
as much as his own boy but that is the way it is with
David   I wish David would wear better clothes
He looks like a smith all the time

11   Nothing much   Mrs Nutt came by but didnt stop
long just to say hello   She is funny   It was
like she hoped I wasnt there and when she said hello
and I answered hello it was like she was taken
aback some way or other   She is funny   We
talked a bit about the declining state of Mrs Hardy
Allens mother then Josie brought me something out
of the house a fan I had asked her to get for me
Mrs. Nutt said hello and was pleased to know her
Calistras sister   Then she went off   Josie says
she looks like a scare that wont scare crows   I
laughed at that

12   Cleaned the attic today with Josie   Came across
a box of Evies things packed away when she was a
little girl for her to have kept safe to look at later
on and think about them and the times they would
remind her of   The way we do looking back on

our journey but Evie wont ever have that my poor darling   I cried and Josie said oh please dont do that   I said Josie you made me laugh yesterday do you remember   She said yes   I said my dear that is the first time I have laughed since Evie died   Thank you   It was so hot up in the attic I think the dust got into my lungs and I cried and coughed   Josie had a pail of clean water with her she took her kerchief and soaked it and wiped off my face with it   I felt better then   Josie is going to be a blessing like Calistra

13 David home today   I dont see how he can bear to go anywhere dressed the way he does wearing those baggy pants all the time   He got in late afternoon went right to the store after supper Josie stayed with me awhile and told me stories about her and Calistra when they were little girls All the things they did over there the other side of town where they live together all the Negro people Calistra still down with the flue Josie said but feels better   It rained hard while we were talking so even though it was time for Josie to go she stayed with me for awhile   I finally had to give her my pairasol   She went home then after making me laugh some more talking about her and Calistra I went to bed and slept well a short nap dreaming which I dont do much that God had decided to change people into rain so they would be happy

14 Charlie is going to come home to stay for a few weeks   David says he is not in very good spirits Nothing unusual about that I'd say

15 Went to
meet Cl
that Joe
grace th
We walk
do you
walking
carrying
you all ri
somethin
Mrs Nutt
I said is
ahead wou
at me a m
back to wo
go after M
If Calistra
Nutt well
am going to
wouldnt he
pointed bro
wear that ri
to the train

16 Charlie is he
when he cam
him not to g
came   But
home   O G
duties this bei

17 Charlie and h
today and I

18 S
I

19

around his straw boater red white and blue
David said well is that the way they carry the flag
in the City   Charlie didnt think it was funny
Didnt laugh a bit   They went on to the store
together this morning David sloppy just stumping
along in his fishing jacket and corderoys with
that pointed brown fishing hat cap whatever it is
tucked down over his eyes and Charlie with him
his son and image but gayly decked out in straw
hat white shoes and striped jacket   The two of
them moving down the street like two boats trying
to get out of the harbour at the same time and
bumping up against each other   They dont understand each other father and son that is where
a woman comes in   I dont think this trip is doing Charlie all that good no matter what it is they
are talking over business or what   Ed is left
there in the City without his brother   I got a
letter from him today he is very lonsum without
Charlie

20   Today was Josies day and I was so glad to see her
She is almost now as much blessing as Calistra
was   She got some soap in her eyes washing
I damped a rag and held her head back and got it
out for her and soothed her eye   She couldn't
keep her eyelid open for awhile it just kept on fluttering and fluttering   Finally she got all right
and was grateful and did the rest of her work
singing

21   Yesterday after I got that soap out of Josies eye
and she finished the washing she was so cheerful
and happy   She told me she liked working for

me and I thought then well I will just do something
good for her poor girl with all that family her and
Calistra the only girls in it it must be something
awful   I took her upstairs to my darling Evies
room   Josie looked about sadly thinking what it
must have been like to live in such a fine room as
this with a mother doing for her and the sunlight
coming in clean and bright through a high window
every morning to wake her up   I have never seen
where Josie and Calistra live exactly but I know it
must be a shack like all those others there   So
I could tell then what she was thinking and I
smiled and said well Josie heres some good news
for you   I opened Evies closet and took out some
of her dresses   Evie and Josie both about the
same size   Josie of course filled out more and her
legs are thicker and torso of course bigger   I
held some of them up against Josie and figured
where they would have to be let out to fit her
My poor Evie who left all these behind   Josie
didnt know what to say just fluttered those big dark
eyes and I chose two of the dresses to fix up for
Josie and told her wed work on them together
Josie took my hand and thanked me   She knows
I mean to do good turns for her now   I held the
dresses up tight against her so it was just like she
had them on already and she got so excited
She is going to be a great blessing this girl   She
is more lively than Calistra but not so fickle I hope
Calistra does Mrs Nutt make up her daughters
dresses for you I suspect not   Josie said you
dont have to do this for me and I said hush Josie
I am glad to   Evie would want me to she is dead
and you are alive

22 Josie will come five days a week now David agreed and I will be able to do the dresses for her and get my work done better maybe this house can look like something decent again   I dont think David liked it much Josie here 5 days but I said if you have your filthy half Indian Joe Waggoner and those good for nothing Moulton brothers around and can pay them to tend store while you go off fishing with Charlie then I can have Josie   Somebody has to help me with all I do my washing and sewing and cooking and cleaning and work on the dresses   David then looked at me kindly and said all right

23 David and Charlie just had a bad argument I knew that would come I think it is about Ed and me in some way   Well I dont understand them

24 I dont feel good today   Cleaned the kitchen and the flues took up the dining room carpet will clean it tomorrow   Worked some in the garden

25 I didnt go to church today   Mavis Grant came by afterwards to tell me William Craig wasnt there neither   David and Charlie grumbling at each other but still went fishing today the Sabbath it doesnt matter to men

26 Josie and I worked all morning on the kitchen walls and the dining room walls   They are looking a little better now   I was so tired and wore out I got dizzy going upstairs and had to stop and hold the bannister hard and then sit down on the steps

Josie said maybe she ought to go try to get David and Charlie but I said no what I needed was just to get up to breathe a little better   Josie helped me up and then into my bedroom   She wanted to go get David but I said no what I needed was my darling Evie to sit by my side and comb out my hair for me and I couldnt help crying then Josie said how do you want it done Ill do it if you want and I showed her and she combed out my hair for me while I sat in my rocker   Calistra has bigger hands but Josie is much more delicate with comb and brush   She sings faster than Calistra did and is a more jumpy girl but she combed out my hair very nicely for me   We measured hands and laughed because mine are bigger   I said Josie are you tired after a hard days work and she looked at me with those big clear dark eyes and said no mam Im not tired   I said well you should be by now   You sit down now and I will do it for you   She was all giggles but I got her into my rocker and combed her hair for her even though she couldnt hardly sit still at first But she calmed down and was something quiet then like Calistra when I got her hair out and opened up so that some of it lay back on my hand and wrist   Josie then set her head back against the chair and became calm and dreamy closed her eyes and let her arms hang down   Bending over her I could smell her breath the sweet wet breath of youth   I combed slower and slower until she sighed and we shared at one touch of the comb on her scalp a moment of true peace   Then I heard Charlie and David stomping around outside the room going up and down the stairs and had to go and fix their supper for them it was that late the time just shot by me   I am worried about Charlie he and David are just at odds over something I knew that is the way it would be   Men

27 Charlie went back to the City today   David stayed out all night at the store drinking with that filthy half Indian Joe Waggoner

28 David wont talk about it Charlies sudden new disgrace and shame and thats all right with me   I have written today to Ed   I hope he will know how to make Charlie realize what a despikable thing he did before he left

29 I wrote to Ed again today said I hoped he would be able to come home 4th of July but didnt say anything more about Charlie   Im sure Ed has more worthy pursuits to ponder these days than that   Charley what a disgrace   David still wont even talk about it

30 After all my worries and fretting about Josie she did come back to day   She says it is all right and she will go on working for me in spite of it all She said for me not to mind what others do and took a pile of washing right out of my hands that minute and went off to do them for me   What a fine girl and god bless her   I wonder if she told Calistra   I wonder what Calistra said if she did

Same day Letter today from Ed   Doesnt say anything about Charlie at all   Just a few words of hello and one of his drawings this time a picture of two

men sitting on a riverbank fishing except they are
asleep behind them their tent is on fire and under
the water a fish is about to take one of the lines
It is very pretty drawing but the fish is all out of
size   It is about five times bigger than the men
are and has huge teeth that such fish dont have
Ed could be a really good enough artist if he could
only get things into the right porportion anyway I
am proud of his talent

July 1   Today in the street I had to walk past William
Craig   He tried to say something to me   He
came up to me straightbacked like some soldier and
opened his mouth to speak to me but thanks to God
I was with friends Mavis Grant and Mrs Phiney
praise be for our support   I could not help but
cry   I must in that moment turn to my dear
friends and they did not fail me   They sheilded
me in my distress and stepped in between staunch
and sturdy and forbid William Craig any pursuit
of evil design on me   They held up their arms
and spoke so loud other people stopped to watch
His soldership crumbled then and his hands shook
and behind that ugly dirty beard his ugly face just
fell   There was lots of people around us in the
blink of an eye and William Craig tried to start
something up with them about me something awful
about my sweet Alice why cant he leave her there
in the grave mangled and torn where he put her
The people bless them would hear none of it and
they took me away almost feinting to Mrs Fanny
Knaps and gave me tea and salts leaving him
standing there gasping trying to say something evil
All the people walked on past and around him like

he was a puddle of water dirty water   Alice my
darling

2 I went to church today the Sabbath   It was a
bright day and very sunny   There have been
two new colored windows stained glass put into
the east wall and the sunlight fell upon me where
I sat   Fell upon me in all that beauty through
the face and torn hands of my saviour Jesus Christ
His white robe has a red and scarlet lining to it
and oh the sky above him into which he is rising
is bright yellow and rich purple with a beautiful
blazing sun behind his glorious head   His eyes
are big and knowing his poor hands bleed red blood
and sunlight as it passes through him and falls upon
me   O he is my salvation   He alone can know
the pain in my heart because he went through it
all there was no drop he did not quaff to the bitter
dregs and yet still rose up the third day into the
purple yellow sky his face radiant his gaze so
majestic his torn hands bleeding but upraised Jesus
Christ who knows my suffering and can still hold
up his hands and mount who is hope and sunlight
The company in the City who makes these windows
should be blessed   William Craig got as far as the
doors   He stopped there   I could tell it was
him there at the door about to come in the way
some people looked quick at me   I sat up
straight and did not move   Mavis Grant told
me he shook his head muttered something his hands
quivering like the leaf turned away at the door
and left the church   The hymns were pleasing
I find it strange that some days you sing better than
others the human voice is funny as the human per-

son some days it sings like the lark and some days it dont   Except of course for Calistra and dear Josie they sing all the time and in that wonderful window right now dear brave Jesus is mounting with my suffering going up to his father in heaven forever   How many women like me will he take with him one day and make them know what triumph is

3   Josie came to work today and David told me both Ed and Charlie will be here tonight for tomorrows doings tomorrow being 4th of July   I did not think Charlie would come back so soon after what happened but he means to   So I said Josie come on lets work some on the dresses   We went up to Evies room my darling how I miss her and I did some fitting for Josie   Journal there are some things I fear to tell you sometimes they are not always decent things I do not think should be said even to you bad bad things   But all along I have meant to be honest with you as I know how
That is why I started you in the first place and so I will put down just what happened so that the good and the bad will be clearly side by side together and not scrambled up like eggs and you have to eat one with the other   All right then
Now today I fitted Josie   One dress was still way too tight it had to be fitted again   Josie had on a cotton thing that made the fitting come out wrong so we had to try the dress on right   I said when we started Josie did he hurt you   You can be frank with me I said and she said again no he didnt not really but of course you know she is afraid to say what really happened   It was the day after

we had combed each others hair journal let me see
now   Wait a minute this is what you are for
after all let me see   Yes youre right it was June
26 we combed each other and June 27 that it happened even if I didnt put it down in writing that
day   June 27 in the morning when Josie was up
to clean the upstairs bedroom all except Charlies
of course he sleeps late when he is home   Charlie
and David too had both been fussy and nervous
when they came home while Josie and I was combing in my room   When Josie left to go home
Charlie stopped her a minute and whispered something in her ear she tried to make a giggle of it
then frowned and went on   Then Charlie ran to
David quick I saw him and whispered something
to David I didnt hear   David just smiled and
shook his head mildly grinning that droopy way
he has said phsaw or something and looked like a
weed without water the way he does   He might
have stopped Charlies lust and disgrace right there
but of course being David he didnt   So anyhow
after breakfast the next morning Josie came to the
house smiling and of her usual good disposition not
knowing what was in store for her   We had our
breakfast David went on to the store I stayed in
the kitchen Charlie was alseep I thought   I got
out my pie dough and apples and laid them out for
myself to fix and bake   I do not know what made
me go upstairs journal   Some kind of very uneasy thing anyway up I go and no Josie cleaning
I call her and she just isnt up there it appears and
so I think a minute and then come on back downstairs   Then I hear some kind of scuffling on the
ceiling in the dining room and thats Charlies room

up there so I think oh oh can this be going on
I go back upstairs stand at Charlies door and call
to him   He answers in a sleepy voice what do I
want   I say nothing just to get in there to see
about something please open the door   He says
let it wait Im still sleepy and I hear the springs of
the bed creek as he turns over   His voice is just
naturally what it would be that time of morning
him asleep and I think what kind of nerves do I
have to jump around the house so and reach this
conclusion   I then say Charlie have you seen Josie
There is no answer   I say Charlie have you see
Josie again and still no answer   I stand there
wondering what to do Im so nervous and shaky and
feel awful   Then it is quiet and I say to myself
well hes gone back to sleep   I wanted to go on
back to the kitchen but I had to try it again just
once more so I say again Charlie is Josie in there
Then bang journal the door flies open Charlie swinging it hard flinging it open so it bangs against
the wall and Charlie standing there filling up the
doorway   He is wearing that striped shirt and a
bow tie and that is all   His cuffs are all open at
the sleeves and he doesnt have nothing else on him
not a stich   He looks at me with blazing eyes
his mouth all twisted up   He glares at me his
own mother like that then swings back away from
the door and oh I see poor Josie on the floor setting
up against the bed with one arm on it like it was
something to cling to   She was lying like that
and she began moaning to herself   It was like
she was drunk had been intoxicated   Her clothes
are in a ring around her middle where her dress has
been pushed up over her legs and her hips and

pulled down off her shoulders   The poor girls
whole body almost exposed that way   Her upper
and lower parts are all bathed in sweat   She
twitches about and about slowly moaning and
groaning not even knowing I am there or what is
happening   Then Charlie calls me awful names
in a terrible whisper and turns about marches to
the bed gets down with Josie and puts his hand on
her person   She twitches again moans and wraps
her arms and legs around him crying so confused
not knowing what to do
Well journal there you have it
I picked up a vase on the table by the door and
threw it at them   I thought how do you get dogs
apart you throw water on them and I was going to
get some and do that but the vase breaking made
Josie see it was me in the room and she tried to
get up   Charlie pulled on her and hauled her
down once more and that crazy thing he hugged
her like a wrestler with somebody in a bear hug
then Josie pinched him or something and got loose
She ran past me out of the room and I slammed
the door on Charlie lying their in his iniquity and
followed Josie into the bathroom where she was on
her knees by the tub crying   She would have
banged her head on it I think   But I held her
tight and then got a rag soaked it in cool water
You did this for me Josie I said wiping her face
you did this once for me do you remember now I
will do it for you   And she said oh oh oh oh but
I calmed her down wiping away the sweat off her
good strong healthy dark body saying now now you
are going to be all right dont you think about Charlie
now not even if he is my own son will I have this

happen to you   I wiped her off good with the
rag soaked it cool again held it against her head
and stomach and chest and legs until she was all
right saying to her no no honey you wont loose
your job not if you want to stay and I for one certainly hope you will Josie now   She said she
didn't know she just wanted to go home now
I said surely just let me dry you off   I did and
helped her get her clothes back on straight and
decent me feeling so sad she was treated so horibly
and that I might loose this girl too as well as Calistra   She went home then   I walked her to
the door gave her some extra wage and said oh Josie
my dear please dont blame me I had no idea Charlie my own son would ever in this world do such a
thing   She nodded and wouldn't say nothing but
she did reach out and press my hand that fine girl
When I got back in the house Charlie was packing
upstairs I could hear him moving around and I
went back to my pie and preserves   When he
come down he was all dressed up within an inch
on his life just like this was exactly the sort of
morning exercise he needed to get him off to a good
start saying he was on his way back to the good
wholesome City   He wouldn't let me say one
word Charlie   Shut up he told me his own mother
and stood there staring at me a long time   He
looked at me so hard and stared so intense with
his eyebrows drawn down close over his eyes strain-
ing to look a dagger through me   Looking at me
so close and hard as if I was vanishing right there
before his eyes and then so hard that look that it
hurt him and it was like his eyeballs had just
turned around in their sockets and he was staring

at himself instead of me   Ive got your number
he said Ive got your number and its an odd one   *
He then looked at my pie dough and preserves and
he took a womans garter Josies surely out of his
pocket and threw in on my kitchen table saying
how do you like those apples Mama grabbed his
bag and went out slamming my kitchen door behind
him with me yelling having found my tongue at
last how could you do such a thing to a fine healthy
young innocent girl like Josie a worker employed
here plunged into such fright and confusion the
poor child
Well then
So today I fitted Josie with poor Evies dress
When because of the fitting Josie took off her cotton piece she was sweaty again a little because of
the fierce heat and I got a towel and rubbed her off
with it   She said she would do it and took the
towel   I asked her then to tell me if Charlie hurt
her at all I really wanted to know and she said he
didnt   I said now Josie dont be that way tell me
did he get it into you at all and she said she didnt
think so it was all so hard to remember   I
grinned and said well Josie the harder it is the easier
you remember it and she laughed at that and hid
her face with the towel   Standing there young
and healthy holding that towel over her face I said
thats good you laugh and so she did her head buried
in the towel and all the good strong muscles of her
body moving around this way and that   Then I
took the towel from her and said just so you dont be
afraid here Josie now hold up her arms   She did
and I slipped poor darling Evies dress on over her
It needed letting out at the hips and the bosum

still and I got my chalk and marked it off   Josie
went ouch   I said honey did I pinch you with
this chalk Im sorry and she said no it just made
her shiver and she laughed again   I finished and
said hold up your arms again and she did and I
stood up on a chair and drew the dress up off of
her so it wouldn't get wrinkled and rub off my
marks   She turned around then and looked up
at me   She has the sweetest face it may be black
but it is a trusting face and how good it makes me
feel   I said honey dont you worry now about
Charlie   He is coming back here for July 4th
but I wont let him bother you and she said all right
and looked up at me   She is only 17 that sweet
thing and it was something looking down on her
holding the dress   It was like I looked down
journal at my own self when I was 17   Like I
stood looking down the years from the age of my
time now on down through my life to the time when
I stood 17 in my room putting on and taking off
dresses in the youth of my body and spirit   I felt
that so strongly I cried a little swaying up on the
chair and Josie said oh what is it now   I said
nothing just that I will always care for you Josie
dear if you want me to   She thought a minute
and wet her lips a minute and said all right   She
reached up to put her hands on my waist and she
laid her cheek like a little child trusting me against
my stomach   Oh how I felt then   I cried some
more and with a sigh threw Evies dress over on
the bed and with both hands pressed the back of
her sweet head to me saying oh what a comfort in
this cold cold life Josie honey   She said all right
then again and wrapped her arms around me tight

where I was standing up on the chair above her
looking down on her sweet youth through all my
age and distance and time   She hugged me and
pressed her face to me   Then in the parlour
journal we both heard David banging on the pianno
Years ago David learned three pieces on the pianno
one of them Farmers in the Dell and there he
was down there playing all three of them loud as
he could   He was home from the store already
the time had flew by it was dinner time already
I held Josie for a minute then got down from the
chair and she got back into her cotton thing and
I said dont you worry honey about the 4th of July
or anything else you are too young and sweet to
bother your head about anything while I am here
She said all right again and I went on downstairs
with her to fix Davids dinner for him before he
broke the pianno banging on it so loud

July 4th This has been a day of excitement   Mr Best we
think he was drowned this morning went over the
Keith River Falls in a canoe poor Mrs Best is
frantic I have been there all day

5th Mr Best not found yet   I staid with poor Mrs
Best this is her great grief not like mine worse in a
way because so aggravating   O how I pity her
my heart aches so   I know how to sympathize
with those that mourn   Ed and Charlie here getting along all right   But the whole town looking
for Mr Best journal dogs lanterns everything
His poor mother and father have come to town
Mrs Albert Maize Mrs Fanny Knap Mrs Raymond
Phiney and I staid there turn and turn about

Mavis Grant too but not as much   And wouldnt
you know Mrs Nutt would show up but she made
everything so confused and jumpy she left soon
Doesnt know how to act in a situation like this at
all   She even had the nerve to say hello to me
from Calistra   I said hello to Calistra through
her from Josie her younger sister and that fixed
Mrs Nutt   Poor Mrs Best she is in a state
They just cant find her husband   Josie had been
so good done all the work while I have been with
Mrs Best

6   Mr Best was found at noon and buried quick at
five oclock   I barely got to the funeral in time
This whole town mourn for him he was such a
nice man so quiet and neat and smiling   Short
and roly poly   How kind he was to me when my
poor Evie went up into the colorful sky with Jesus
He was her Sunday School Superintendant A B Best

7   Well journal I guess you want to know all about
this excitement and I will tell you   It was some
4th of July let me say that right away   Ed and
Charlie got here late on the night of the third
Charlie came in by himself with David who went
to the train   I said wheres Ed Charlie said he
stopped off by the church   I said what   He
said Ed wanted to stop off by the church   I
thought that was funny but was glad   God works
in mysterious times as well as ways this being almost midnight   We had some coffee and sure
enough twenty minutes later carrying his bag Ed
comes in the front door and said yes he had been
to the church   Told me thats right it did me

some good asked me if I had seen the new window
stained glass and did I like it   I said surely I
did   He said he knew the man who designed it
and it was made at his glass works   I was glad
to hear it   Ed smiled and went on to bed   I
praise God that perhaps he is bringing in my sons
O let me see that day let me see it

Well after lunch on the 4th of July we went on out
of doors the four of us together   Ed wore a
jacket and looked all right except the sleeves as
always too short for his long skinny arms   David
even put on his best and only suit to please me and
Charlie well Charlie mad as I am at him right now
he did look fine   Striped jacket and boater with
a three colored band   Shoes whiter than snow
Pants pressed and creased firm as the edges of
boards in a lumber yard   Hair all combed slicked
down and his bright freckle face shining   Swinging a cane with a gilded tip and an ivory handle
Mad as I am at Charlie I will say he was something
to look at on the 4th of July   Several times we
had to stop while people wanted to say hello and
some who didnt know find out who this was

The parade went off all right   Bobby Taylor fell
off a haywagon and broke his wrist in front of the
bank but thats expected that poor little boy is always banging himself up some way   Nobody
drunk this time at all   After parade we all went
out to Keith River for the main celebration and
festivity   It was to be quite a thing   Several
of the fire companies in the state got together and
decided to give us all a show that would make us
see what it really is the 4th of July   They had
a lot of wagons and boats out there at Keith River

Keith River you know is dammed up above the place where we all went and it swells out into almost a lake there now and people can swim and rest there   The Falls are down about half a mile the other side below   Well the fire companies had four or five large open boats out there with soldiers in the uniforms of the American Army in two of the boats and soldiers in British Red in the other three   A soldier stood in the front of each boat waving whichever one of the two different flags American or British he was to wave and the brave soldiers acted out the battle that took place around here somewhere then   I have heard about it since I was a little girl but I still dont have it straight I dont think they do either anyway it was a fine show   The British boats outnumbering us came in hard and strong but our brave men bore down pulled mightily on their oars and outran them in circles   Then the British pulled out long wicked rifles and so did our brave boys and they all fired Now journal when they did that those fire company wagons had put powder all over everywhere and boom there were really scary and fine explosions everywhere   Smoke poured out on the lake and you thought the whole nation was going up in smoke fire and explosion   Then the band started playing cymbels banging and a church choir too and on the water behind all that smoke out from under canvas in the boats came dainty pretty girls all dressed up gayly each with a pairasol   The men in the smoke shed those uniforms and were out there suddenly in sailing suits and striped jackets some of them like Charlies and they all laughed and sang out there on the lake part of Keith River

The Mayor got up waved to them and us saying
something we will always fight for this life we love
you see that is the meaning of 4th of July Independence Day   This proof of that meaning of
4th of July made its impression   A fine and dramatik spectikle especially the lovely explosions and
the sudden change from soldiers fighting into pretty
girls and handsome men   Every boat then of
course had up its American flag   The band
played and played it was wonderful and made you
so proud but then Edmund Waggoner come into the
scene   Journal I have already told you about
filthy Joe Waggoner that David likes so much and
who he lets handle the store for him sometimes
Well Edmund Waggoner is three times filthier than
Joe Waggoner   No five times   He is supposed
to be Joe Waggoners grandfather   He is the
meanest old man around here for miles has been for
years its the same Indian blood in him Joe Waggoner
has   Old Edmund Waggoner lives in a shack four
miles out of town   I have passed by it sometimes
it isnt far from the road   You have to pass it
going to the City   Edmund Waggoner there he
lives all alone with his dogs   He has long black
gresy hair wears clothes so horible and filthy you
cant even see what kind they were once let alone
are now   He is a terrible old man who has nothing to do with nobody except his dogs   Keeps
nothing but mongrel bitches four of them   Eats
with them and it is said and I believe it the man
sleeps with them all four mongrel bitches on the
floor in that awful shack   If it has a floor   I
certainly would never go in there to see   He is
something should have been dealt with long ago

but he is only part Indian after all and has his property rights like the rest of us   What he does to stay alive is just trap and fish thats all   He will come into town with furs and skins wintertime and fish in the summer and get his goods   Nobody fools around with him not even his own grandson Joe almost as filthy but not nearly so fierce

Joe Waggoner jumps out of the way when that old man comes down the street his old head stuck out and glaring that long gresy hair flapping and one two three sometimes four of those bitches heeling behind him like some harem   When Edmund Waggoner passes you on the street you have to hold your nose I mean it   One time I stood next to him in the street because I couldn't help it was caught talking to somebody and that old man bent over like a hook most of the time well he stood straight yawned and stretched   His breath was something terible and when he lifted his arms stretching and flapped them back against his skinny body hard as some knot the stink of the man made me plain sick I almost feinted   He has always lived alone and he hates everybody women especially   He is a terible thing the only good he does is you can set your clock by him during the summer and fishing season   He comes down Keith River in his canoe and passes through the swell here in the lake right dead through the center of it at the same time every day same place and that never fails when there is fishing to be done

He has fished up above in the early morning and by afternoon he is on his way downriver to fish the dusk there   Hits the Keith River swell at 3 pm Every day it is the same

Well

It so turned out that he came through during that
celebration 4th of July   Now David tells me he
saw a little spot upriver out of the corner of his eye
and looked at his watch and saw it was almost 3 pm
Now he forgot about it for a minute then when he
looked again the spot was bigger and he knew who
it was coming because it was about 3 pm and all
David says he just naturally thought old man Waggoner would backpaddle and watch it all or pull up
on the bank and observe this fine patriotic scene
and demonstration so David didnt pay it any mind
he just kept watching the American soldiers beat
the British   Right about then the firing com-
menced the explosions the band played and the
boys and girls changed out there on the water into
beautiful young ladies fine young men all in gay
happy celebration   The band played Yankee
Doodle and the pairasols twirled and the smoke
drifted off and up so pretty but when David looked
again at that spot he saw it was a spot no longer
but old man Edmund Waggoner himself completely
big as life now and paddling his canoe right ahead
slowly but steady dead center of the lake his eyes
looking neither right nor left not hardly blinking
just like there was no one there at all and him on
his usual path downriver his possession and pride
David nudged me and told me and I saw the old
man then his gresy hair and hooked nose and them
cold mean proud eyes   The flags was waving and
the music gay and then somebody else saw him too
and somebody yelled something at him funny watch
out old man youll get shot something like that
The girls in the boats right then was throwing flow-

45

ers on the water and singing some pretty song but one by one they looked at each other and stopped after he sailed past the first boat   They tried to keep on but just didnt and in no time everybody was suddenly quiet as could be   Old Man Waggoner just paddled on   Taking his canoe right through them   There was then for some reason quite a hush everywhere   He just sailed right along distaining the whole event   That is until one of the girls some pretty young thing laughed made a face at him stuck out her pretty tongue and held her nose and laughed when he passed by her   He turned his head just a mite and spit a great chunk of something awful I hope it was only tobacco all over her pretty gay dress   She squealed turned to a brave young soldier standing next to her but he wasnt about to say a word to Edmund Waggoner who paddled on went right through them past the American flags the rejoicing youth and gay celebration him dirty and stinking with his fishline trailing behind and his four mongrel bitches standing up in the front and back of his boat as distainful as he was   It was quiet as he passed   All the people on the banks were just very quiet until David said out loud with a catch in his voice husky he said Well God bless that old man   The soldiers and pretty girls just stared at that canoe going by opened their pretty mouths gaping   Then on the riverbank where all the people were watching after David spoke or at about the same time somebody said Thats right thats right   Somebody else yes yes thats it thats what its all about July 4th   Thats Independence day for you hooray   Soon a few people clapped and there was a cheer or two then before you knew it everybody was clapping their hands laughing and cheering that awful old man   Even the Mayor had to smile weak like and nod his head and wave to the canoe going by   The soldiers the girls the boats the flags looked plain foolish   He never turned his head once after he spit Edmund Waggoner he just went on downriver to fish that was what he did every day and that was what he was going to do today and away he went straight as a plumbline that terible creature

Oh journal my hand hurts   Shoo I get tired writing so much but I want it down for you the way it was

Now there was a canoe and a flat bottom or two banked on the river   A B Best got up threw off his coat and in vest and white shirtsleeves jumped into a canoe one I believe belonged to Ernest White anyway he was suddenly in it and off paddling away just like old man Waggoner   Paddling with his head up a funny look in his big wide open eyes A B Best a plump little man with pale tiny hands and bad feet   Had to wear funny shoes and a strap around his back all the time too I think

But he whaled away with that paddle in that canoe upsetting himself almost two or three times you could tell this wasnt his sort of thing jumping into canoes he didnt know much about them   People laughed and made a little fun of him all flushed in the face like he was pink and sort of bug eyed filled with that great emotion of some sort whatever it was   Now journal where there was something made you hush about Edmund Waggoner there was something just pitiful about A B Best after the life he has lived in town like all the rest of us jumping

in that canoe and setting off like that   People
laughed at him and soon he was out of sight
What got into him they wondered laughing   Mrs
Best was so mortified I never saw a woman that
figity and upset blushing and holding out her hands
in amazement saying well you see well well you see
The band went to it again striking up bravely and
it sounded a little flat   But we all had a nice
time eating and mingling for an hour or so but
David had a puzzled look on his face I saw that
After an hour David went off with Ed but I didnt
pay it much mind   I watched Charlie gay as he
could be carrying on making people laugh girls
blush men frown standing about shiny swinging his
stick   I was talking to Mrs Fanny Knap and
Mrs Best when David and Ed come back looking
serious and got some men together   They told
Mrs Best that Ernest Whites canoe had been found
just below Keith River Falls with no A B Best in it
So the search started   They went to find Edmund Waggoner where he was fishing downstream
He said no he never saw no A B Best leave me
alone   They did but couldnt find the man anywhere and night fell upon them   They then went
that night to Edmund Waggoners shack and found
him not the hero of the afternoon but just a dirty
old man half naked and filthy drunk lying down
with his dogs his mongrel bitches   They couldnt
get no more out of him than before
He got mad grabbed his shotgun tried to shoot
them but they got it away from him gave him a
drink and he quieted down said again no he didnt
no nothing about no fool A B Best trying to catch
up with him in a canoe   Said he took his canoe
around the Falls by land like always and saw no

one coming after him   David was there and he
says he knew then the old man was telling the truth
for this reason   Even if he had drowned poor
A B Best that old man wouldnt care who knew it
So the search went on even though some of the
men were for doing something about old Edmund
Waggoner   The search went on until noon yesterday July the 6th   Then it stopped   A B
Best went over the Falls all right   He must
have been caught under water or something and
came up only then   He was a sight   Cut to
pieces and all the blood drained out of him by
the running water   They said his clothes was
torn and rotting and he was bloated bad   Them
funny heavy shoes he had weighed him down even
if he had been conscious when he went over the
Falls   His coat and shirt was torn and the strap
he wore for his aching back was cut even and busted
He had swallowed a lot of water I guess because
his roly poly stomach was like a ballon and he was
almost as round as he was tall and long lengthwise
They did the best they could and buried him quick
I got to the funeral just as they was all going into
the church carrying him in and wouldnt you know
down the street passed old Edmund Waggoner carrying a line of fish to the store   He looked at the
coffin spit and said not a word   Thats the story
journal it was some 4th of July

8 Fanny Knaps granddaughter baptised at the Episcopal church   Mrs Hardy Allens mother taking
her last gasps poor thing but then she is over ninety
way over ninety how does one manage that I
wonder

9 Tired yesterday didnt write   Today Sunday and in church Rev Bayley made a blunder   He was preaching to us about the clear call   He thought a minute and said before thinking long enough you know A B Best our dear departed friend must have had something like that to get into that canoe the way he did   It was not a fortunate sermon   You could maybe see what Rev Bayley was trying to get across but then you also saw in minds eye A B Best in his frenzy almost upsetting that canoe bug eyed and you know what happened to him   Besides poor Mrs Best was there she cried and Rev Bayley got upset and stammered and made a wrong choice again trying to push his point on home and would just keep talking about the clear call   Everyone was so uneasy   He came out of it finally seeing how bad it was what a mess he was making and called for the hymn then William Craig nowhere to be seen

11 Got very tired at Mrs Bests house   Have been resting today and back to my old thoughts again when shall I see light

12 Have been working hard today   Josie singing and doing the wash   Letter from the boys in the City saying they enjoyed their 4th of July my fine sons Charlie signed the letter love Charlie and I am not mad at him any more how can I be   Ed drew his usual picture on the back of the letter except this time a big firecracker about to go off   Except the firecracker is the body of A B Best the fuse comes out his ear and he is lighting it himself

I worry about Ed he could draw sensible things so
well if he would just put his mind to it

13   Worked hard today   Josie thinking about something else I had to make her do the wash over
She laughed about it   Poor girl with her unfor-
tunate background she just cant understand why
I have our clothes washed so much   Hardly
knows what real cleanliness is but a fine person in
spite of that   This afternoon have been comforted in spite of my thoughts while reading a book
given to Mrs Best   Called Our Friend in Heaven
She didnt want to read it gave it to me   It is
such a beautiful book   I was reading it this
afternoon when I went to sleep   Then Josie came
up and combed my hair

14   Stopped by the Episcopal church this afternoon
Dont know why   Nobody there   It is a comforting sanctuary too fancy of course   Stained
glass but not so bright and colorful as ours   I
thought of going there some time but I guess not
It was quiet tho and peaceful   If only Evie and
Alice could have gone there with me how close I
still feel to them both of them my darling girls
Went to see Mrs Best surprized to see her so calm
now

15   Josies mother is sick Josie wont be able to come for
awhile   I said well Josie how long and she said
she didnt know   My heart sank   But I then
said what can I do for you Josie in this painful time
and she said nothing acted queerly   I said well
be brave then and hugged her and she went on home

Maybe her mother will die soon she is old enough and Josie will be back soon   But it is hard to bear the thought of young and beautiful Josie stricken with grief   That body bent   I would comfort you out of my own grief Josie   For it is considerable isnt that right journal

16   Sabbath but did not go to church at all   Everyone there will be making so much out of Mrs Best She deserves her comfort but I cant help noticing she bears her grief a little too well too soon   Last Sunday when I walked in nobody turned their heads they were all waiting for Mrs Best to come in   William Craig you have missed your chance you could have come on to church that day and nobody would have cared about you and me at all   How quick they are to comfort you how quick to leave you for the sorrows of somebody else Expect you to forget too   Maybe Mrs Best will be that way but not me   I have known more than just a husband gone though I know that too Edward dead me a young helpless woman   Then my girls   Losing a husband and losing children is different Mrs Best different different

17   Today David put his arm around my shoulders and said old girl lets take a trip   He thinks that is going to do this old girl a lot of good   I do not care much about going   All David will do is fish He got a new brown pointed fishing hat and he has attached a thin net thing like a womans veil He stood wearing it swinging his arm like he was casting with a rod   I said David what in the world   He said I think I have finally won my war with the deerflys   Grinning like he had just

discovered America   O David David youngest
of all my children

18   We are at cousin Hollins today   Will stay here
the night   Didnt I tell you journal David fishing today out all day caught two little perch thats
all

22   Stayed at Hollins two days now at cousin Marions
Have met some pleasant people it is very beautiful here in summer   Tomorrow we will all drive
to see cousin Lydia Loomis   Jennie and Davids
Aunt Mary Turner will be there and goodness knows
who else

25   Stayed with Lydia Loomis again tonight   David
having good time with the relatives very polite and
even talkative to the women but out fishing with the
men whenever he can get them to go with him which
is most of the time   I worry about the store
David says never you mind that thats my job but I
think of Joe Waggoner keeping the store and fret

29   Have seen so many people   So tired of it
David still going strong   Tomorrow we go to
Davids cousin Anson Ayers place for a reunion of
both sides of relatives   David has talked the
whole thing up I wish he hadnt   Spent this day
with Myron and Belle my side of the family they
are nice farmers   Have a comfortable house here
A great place for fruit and musquetoes

30   They are all there in the yard now while I write
So many people I never thought there were so many
so close to us   Anson Ayers and his wife Sadie

put out a big spread   Those of us who got here
in the morning held a family service this being Sunday   Anson Ayers read from Ecc the wonderful
passage about a time for this and a time for that
He said I guess this is a time for coming together
looking at me and smiling   David nudged me
with his shoulder and when I looked David was
smiling too   But oh David he had his deerfly hat
on all the time   I told him to take that thing off
and he sighed and did   Then in the afternoon
they came all the rest   O so many cousin Marion
and the Hillin part of her family Lydia Loomis
Aunt Mary Turner Jim and Wray Warford and
their four little boys who fight all the time what will
they be like in ten years   Myron and Belle Edna
Ayers who is Ansons sister and her three children
nice little girls   Molly Turner and her two brothers good looking men each with wives and and
babies born days apart only and jokes about which
is which and whos is whos all of that   The Able
Fullers and some of theirs came in a big bunch together with a wagonload of children all talking
laughing the Fullers make a prize of being comical
it was funny only just a little while   I got so tired
By afternoon one hour ago they was all milling
about talking and watching the host of children
rushing in and out of the house and yard fighting
most of the time skipping around sometimes and
yelling   One of them just staring at it all so
many people and children   One little girl she was
I dont know whose she just shook her head and sat
down on the porch steps   I said to her honey you
getting tired out   She said yes a little bit   She
has long yellow hair like Evies was and I said well

what do you think of all of this   She said it
makes me want to sit down   I said honey thats
just exactly it and came in here journal to write
But David came in after me got me and nothing
would do but I go back onto the porch   He stood
there with me took off his fisherman cap waved it
with one arm put the other arm around me and said
just look   I said what do you think I have been
doing for the past week   He said look said it as
dramatik as David ever is waving his hat and staring at all the people our kin moving about eating
Ayers food calculating with each other kidding each
other being placid as humans can which means by
this time there was a lot of backbiting and some of
the children were running around wild and Anson
Ayers and his wife were utterly exhausted and the
sun was about to go down   David thought it was
wonderful and I tried to feel the way he did   I
remembered how when I was a child like these running about in the dusk as evening came on   I remembered what it was like then staying out from
supper as long as you could   It was a tasty time
The dusk hid all our faces and we ran and bumped
into each other in the dark fall of evening journal
flailing arms and falling down running and getting
up the boys chasing us and us running between
them and around them hiding behind trees   Face-
less children thats it in that tasty time you never
knew just how long it would last it was time
stolen in the evening dusk before being one by one
called in to supper   I remembered that and
smiled and tried to look with happiness on all the
pieces of the families spread out in the Ayers yard
before us   David held his hat down very care-

fully at his side   He looked at me with what dignity he has and said you see honey you see we are all one thing just repeated over and over you see
Then he stared and coughed and coughed took his arm away from me blushed and went to the edge of the porch to blow his nose with his open hand
David   He means well   I looked and I saw
I said David you know I am obliged to you for this
He said nothing just looked out over the yard said it was like the flag spangled with the stars of our people then laughed at himself when I did
There they were its true talking fussing fighting arguing laughing running   It made him so happy and calm but not me   I took his deerfly hat out of his hand and with a smile put it back on his head and came back in here journal   Yes we are all one thing repeated and repeated but what thing journal what thing

August 1   I am on the train going to the City   Day before yesterday at the Anson Ayers when I was finishing writing Mrs Wray Warford who has the four little boys came in and sat down with me   She was a very sympathetic warm person and very good and kind to me   She remembered Evie had met my darling four or five times   David came in and stood by for a minute then went out again   Then he came back in a while and said well we best go on back home and I said you go David I want to go to the City to see my boys my own sons and David said all right   This is a good train I am on   Nice people here in the car nobody acting up   Its a dark ride though   Outside there is no moon   I

wont get to the City until late had to send telegraph
ahead   I look out the train window now   They
have night lights on inside here and in the windows
I see people reflected like in mirrors but also the
night outside and the things in the dark whizzing by
Such speed

2 Came to the City last night   Charlie and Ed met
me at the depot along with Mr James Hartwell old
friend of Edward my early husband who lives here
I will stay with James because the boys dont share
the same rooms any more and this way I dont
have to choose between them I think thats best
James and his wife seem glad to see me   He has
held up well James   I remember him and Edward
talking and talking late into the night younger full
of energy   He still has some of it left I can see
Only thing is this is the first time I have seen him
since he came to Alices funeral it was pretty hard

3 Had an interesting day but dont think I can stay
here with James he wants to talk about them too
much and wants to say things about Edward and
Alice it will do me no good and will kill me if it
goes on any more   I want to spend time with my
boys

4 Have spent this evening with the boys   We went
to a band concert a fine welcome from them to me
My Welcome to the City   Charlie is sure a
dresser these days

5 I am staying with Charlie this week at his boarding
house   Run by lady name of Wilson Fay Wilson

and she is divorcing poor thing   Took a fancy to me and we talked most of the morning   I have a nice enough room I suppose   Ed is going to take me to the museum this afternoon   I cant find out why my boys do not share their living quarters any more neither one being married   Something they just dont talk about

6   Went to the museum with Ed yesterday   Saw a lot of very interesting things whale bones and wagon wheels among others   Went to big Union Church this morning with my boys   I felt fine going in with them but I must say the preacher was no good Hes a man with wool in his mouth   No sense at all nothing he said   Talked about the difference between each of the gospels how this proves that Spoiled the whole hour of being gathered together in Gods name   A good preacher has to comfort his people who need him   He stood up there comforting himself   I dont think Ill go there again

7   I dont like Charlies boarding house so well now It is small and mean really but Fay Wilson is a nice enough person but very sharp tongued   She says she is not going to let me talk about Evie any more that I must be as happy as possible while here   I think it is the best possible thing I could do to come here the boys are so glad to have me in the City Even Charlie is nice to me now and of course Ed loves me as he always has in his quiet way   I pray we may be spared to each other for a long time I could not live if either of them should be taken from me

8 Helped Fay Wilson today with her flowers she raises
in long green boxes   Getting them arranged for a
horicultural fair here

9 Am making Charlie some shirts out of fine cloth I
got downtown   Fay Wilson lets me use her sewing machine its a good one   Charlie is glad I am
making them for him only he is not happy with his
work I can see that   He doesnt like selling dry
goods much   Poor boy he is alone in this city
with nothing but one brother and bright clothes to
cheer him up   He keeps talking about the time
when I have to go back home and leave him here
He does not seem very well contented here   I tell
him no wonder

10 I do not see how Charlie can board here as I said its
no wonder he is not contented   I went into his
room yesterday when he was at work and they just
dont keep it well enough for him   The furniture
is not of any quality at all the carpet hasnt been
taken up in years   God only knows whats under
that thing   I spoke firmly to Fay Wilson about
it and while I was at it spoke about the man who
lives right next to Charlies room plays the accordian
all the time that just cant be allowed how can my
boy sleep

11 Today I went to see Ed where he works in the glass
factory   He was so nice to me   Showed me all
around the place   Opened up his big heavy green
books he works in pointed all the rows of figures he
keeps track of   Took me around to where they
make the glass what a lot of work it is just to have

something nice to drink out of   All the men stopped work just a minute to show me glass being made   They showed me how and I blew a little cup and they are going to give it to me later   Ed wondered if I was homesick wondered about the boarding house   I said if Charlie can stand it I guess I can for a few more days

12 Tonight Charlie didnt come in at all   I waited up for him late and then got Fay Wilson up told her she just had to do something   She wasnt nice to me then   Im afraid she is a vulgar woman after all   There is a lot of noise in some of these rooms late at night

13 Ed came this morning   He lives in the Strand Hotel got me a nice room down the hall from him He rented me a sewing machine to finish Charlies shirts on   I hope to do that today but it is so hot and noisy here

14 Charlie came this morning he has quit work at the dry goods store and is going into the selling line He said he was sorry about Fay Wilson being so vulgar and promised me he would find himself another place to live soon   I gave him the shirts Today I got some wonderful silky materials and am going to make dressing gowns for both my boys

15 Worked on the dressing gowns today

16 Today I went to the public library

17 Ed and Charlie rented a span of horses   They
drove me out to get chestnuts   When we came
back I checked them both again for measurement
for the dressing gowns   They will be a perfect fit
each darling boys how I love to work for them

18 What a lonly day   Ed took me to dinner here in
the hotel what prices

19 Worked on the dressing gowns   Ed took me to
the print works here it was interesting   Charlie
had to work

20 Rained again I couldnt go to church   Charlie had
to work again I told Ed it wasnt right to work on
the Sabbath   True enough he said but sometimes
you have to   We had dinner in the hotel same
prices

21 These dressing gowns will be fine garments   Both
boys at work   I hope they dont wear themselves
out in their professions   I will say this for David
he knows how to do his work and get in his fishing
too   I had to eat alone tonight

22 Ed came today Charlie too   They couldnt stay
with me long Charlie has a sellers meeting Ed said
he just wasnt feeling well   I dont like the waitresses in the hotel dining room they dont bring the
right thing when you want it   At least it didnt
rain today

23 Have been to see Charlie today he has been sick
with his stomach cramps and bad nerves   That

Fay Wilson was nowhere around neither oh my poor
Charlie so sick and alone

24   Charlie quite sick how he suffers with his stomach
and nerves   I try to do for him but it makes him
so nervous I am worried about him

25   Ed doesnt feel good these days Charlie still sick I
am so lonly   Journal it is funny even the horses
are sick here in the City   Thats the truth they
are   They have Eppigootic plague here   It is
amusing to see different ways they get packages
carried   Milk cart just passed down in the street
drawn by two men   Oxen are being used instead
of horses

26   Ed came this evening   I showed him the dressing
gowns   We ate in the dining room poor Ed scrib-
bling drawings on a pad with a long pencil holding it
all sorts of ways   I said Ed draw me a flower
why dont you and he did   A lovely little mari-
gold he said it was and it almost looked like one all
right   I said thats fine and then he took it back
and drew one single eye behind the stem so it looked
like the flower was growing out of the eyeball   I
didnt say anything if he wants to be frivolous about
it thats all right it is his hobby after all not mine
He had to leave the table coughing   Went to his
room

27   Visited the public library today   Charlie and Ed
could not come   Their dressing gowns are almost
ready but oh my back

28 This will be a day long to be remembered on account of the great fire in the City   Not only by me but by thousands it has been terible   Many that went to rest last night rich men have awakened this morning paupers everything lost   Thousands are thrown out of work and all employment   The streets are full of crying children   I woke up to it in the dead middle of the night   I saw moving red shadows behind the blinds and shades of my window   I jumped out of bed my bare feet just slapped the floor ran and pulled back the blinds and shades merciful Saviour what a sight   Behind the roofs a great blazing climbing thing   Fire Bells began to clang and in the streets people ran around   Because of the sick horses it was a long time before anything could be done just bucket brigades at first they say   It burned all night and is still burning but will not come here thank the good Lord   Ed came in an hour after I woke up had been out doing what he could was all grimy and dirty coughing too   He was wore out   I sat him down gave him a pan of cool water and a clean rag and he washed himself off and felt better   His shirt was too torn up to mend   We watched through the windows not knowing how bad it was until this morning   It is pretty bad   It didnt get near Charlies boarding house though and Ed is all right except for his weakness from fatigue

29 Went today to Union Church here in the City for a special service   Filled and packed   The preacher a fine man not that other one gave a fitting sermon called upon us to trust God and stand aside in the path of his cataclysms   Many people with

bandages all over them burned in the face and
hands a lot

30 The funerals have started here   There have been
so many of them all I had to do to pay my respects
to the suffering people of the City was to go out the
doors of the Strand Hotel and go in the first church
I saw the services being held one right after the
other   Went to several   Saw four burials also
in the great Semetary   What a short time it has
been since I was here in the City with my darling
Evie buying her things and showing her the sights
Alice too   Now today I stood in the ruined City
and the air was dry and full of drifting white ashes
blown around with black ones   Truly we do not
know what tomorrow will bring   O the thought
of losing my boys it runs into my heart pierces it
like a needle   I will wait for Ed to get home from
the glass works and then take him right away to see
Charlie   We must comfort each other we must

31 Ed was tired wouldnt go to see Charlie   I ate in
the dining room how nasty those waitresses are   I
went to take a book back to the public library   It
was closed   I had a hard time finding my way
back   Got lost three or four tries finally saw the
sign Strand Hotel it made me feel even more lost
what kind of home is that to be struggling so to get
to   So many of the people in the streets now
It is still hot summer they sit in the ashes and ruins
many of them drinking   Some even laughing
The great fire of their city has been put out at last
but it still glows in them burns them poor people
Tomorrow I am going to get my boys and go to

church and give thanks to God and pray for people
still burning

Sept. 1   They couldnt go to church with me   Charlie still
stomach sick Ed has to be at the glass works   I
said Ed we must pray for those who suffer   Ed
wouldnt listen   Said I should not see Charlie that
Charlie loves me so much I worry him living here
these days alone in the dangerous City   Then he
had to go to work there was nothing I could do was
there journal   O what if I lost my darling boys
O the thought of that

2   Have been packing my trunk today   How my
heart aches when I think of leaving my boys but I
must   Ed says Charlie dont want to see me any
more   The thought of me in discomfort and such
makes him worse Ed says   Ed will do his best for
Charlie that is the way I brought them up   I just
cant eat in that dining room again   I am packing
today going home tomorrow

3   Ed just left   I have to wait another day   Got
a telegraph message from David saying no dont
come home today come tomorrow   I gave Ed the
dressing gowns finished last night   Splendid garments fit for my sons I had them both laid out on
the table here when Ed came in   Ed said he
would take Charlies to him   Maybe I will go to
the public library once more

4   Am on the train   The trees outside go by fast
like days

5 Got home yesterday in the afternoon   Left the
City that morning   David met me and when we
came home to the house I found it all brightened up
and looking so pleasant and cheerful   Everything
was clean and scrubbed the windows was opened
and had new shades and the curtains all clean and
white   I said David is this why you wanted me
to stay that extra day   He said yes then sat in
the porch swing newly painted and fooled with a
screwdriver and some kind of lock   I stood there
happy about the house and started to go in   I
didnt mean to have this happen but my home was
so pleasant and cheerful I could not but think and
say O my darling Evie not here to meet me in such
a lovely house such a wonderful hour as this   In
vain did I listen for her footsteps coming down the
stairs and her sweet voice saying mother how glad
I am that you have come   David threw the lock
on the floor of the porch and spent the night at the
store mad

6 The house is pretty damp   David did his best but
the upstairs bedrooms and mine downstairs were
closed all that time only Davids bedroom used
The dining room closed up too   My plants are
pretty well used up

7 My friends have been to see me many of them
Sometime I wish no one would come   I want to
be alone and think all the time but I know that
would not be good for me   Josie came today
I was not as glad to see her as I thought I would be
She looks a little worn   She did her washing

quietly and went home   Her mother still alive
I dont care

8   There is a lot to do in this house

9   Rev Bayley came today   Spoke to me for an
hour about the humble life being submissive to the
will of God   I like him so much he is such a fine
man such a great Christian   Took up the carpets
in both downstairs bedrooms spent the afternoon
beating them out

10   O journal   Today I read a letter   It was to
David from Ed   It was lying on the porch swing
and I had it up and reading it when David came
rushing back down the street knowing he had left
it there and didnt mean to on his way to work
He saw me reading it and stopped and let me finish
Three pages journal about Evie   It began saying he is not going to listen anymore to Charlies
talk about me whatever that means   Then the
rest of it three pages all about Evie   My poor
boy how unreconciled he is to her death never have
I felt more wicked about my own grieving than
after reading Eds letter   He just raved and raved
He sees her inside the glass things at the works
he wrote   He tries to draw something and she
is always in it somewhere he wrote even if it is
only some dog he draws or a cat or a insect
David had not meant for me to see that letter but
I had so he waited and let me read it once I had
it in my hands open   I felt so terible about my
own grief Ed having to bear this all the time his
own grief so powerful   Him of course silent about

it as the grave not like Charlie running around
having fits   O this tore my heart this letter
It did seem to me I would do something awful   I
told David yes   I said yes this is right I feel just
like this here just like Ed   I have only been pretending up to now   I said submissive I have been
I have up to now   I said David oh I have played
long enough I have been submissive long enough
O how I raved God only knows how near I was to
reaching insanity but I could not stop   Not only
must I lose my two children all I have but I must
pretend to submit to it O how I raved and how
dangerous it was   David just kept quiet how
calm he was while I walked through the rooms
It did seem to me my heart and head were bursting
like that bad piece of glass at Eds glass works one
the blower blew too full and it popped apart throwing little drops of melting hot glass on the brick
floor   When my grief was spent I was so weak
I had to set down for a long time   David talked
and talked and talked   Then finally he quit

11   Have been quite sick today

12   Rev Bayley has been here today   I didnt have
much to say   He left soon

13   Didnt feel right all day

14   Rained today cloudy and heavy   I dont think I
see things right   Seems to me I have to squint
now all the time   I should be seeing things easier
than I do   David says I must think about glasses
but thats not it

15 Thunderstorm this afternoon   Rain and lightening swept over us in great flashes and rain torrents blown sideways by the wind   A sycamore tree felled across the road its branches down in the street   I saw it struck and felled   Heard the great crack as it went down the wind and the rain and thunder and the dazzling lightening all such power has made me feel some better   It is still raging out there but I am going to take a nap now

16 Today the sun came out   It was lovely   Everything so fresh   They are clearing away the sycamore tree now with horse wagon and tackle David is helping them he furnished the tackle from the store and knows all about such doing   He stands out there like he was some great doctor of medicine and this a life or death operation saying all right men easy there and hold it and here she goes up up and I cant look at him   The storm is over the sun is out and the grass so green everything so beautiful I am still sick the storm did not help me the way it helps the beautiful world brings it to a great rage and loosening of lightening bolts thunder and torrents of rain   It would be better I was like that then afterwards I could be fresh and clean again like flowers and rain   O God will this grief never end

17 I stayed in bed today   Josie brought me my meals

18 Rev Bayley came today   I tried to ask him about people and thunderstorms   About becom-

ing rain and washed grass about the stricken tree
He did not know what I was talking about   O
how I wish I could do better than this could put
down here just what I truly feel just what I mean
But I cant why   Some reason   Something
holds me back something does not want it   For
me to say all I know is true

19   This morning Josie brought me my breakfast   I
woke up and there she was standing over me holding the tray saying here is your breakfast   I
thought oh Josie I haven't seen you in so long it
seems not really how is your mother   Bedridden
still Josie said otherwise has her spirit up   How
do you manage I asked   She said she and Calistra have it worked out the brothers help some and
there is somebody always with her   I thought
about that a minute and then had the bitter thought
well she is better off than I am why worry about
her   I did not eat much breakfast   Josie was
taking the tray when I saw her dress was worn
through at one shoulder just a bit   You could see
the skin   I said Josie we have forgotten about
your dresses honey   She said oh thats all right
I said no you come back upstairs to Evies room in
a little while   She said all right and went back
to the kitchen with the tray   I got up a little
weak but not too bad put on my gown and went
into my precious darling Evies room had a little
trouble getting up the stairs but not much
Worked on Josies dress finished it sat and waited
for her   After the longest time she did come
climbing the stairs to me   I said here honey your
dress is all ready for you put it on   She said all

right and started to undress   I said no over there
by the mirror where my sweet Evie dressed herself
Josie went over there and stood by Evies chest
and mirror and took off her cotton dress   I said
Josie I think you have gained some weight honey
What where she said twisting around looking down
at herself   I said here and showed her   She
has gained several pounds around the hips   I
turned her around and said look in the mirror see
She said oh that always happens when I worry
I rubbed her hips with my palms and said Josie
maybe I can rub those pounds right off for you
She giggled and held up her arms and said maybe
I could   I showed her where her bosum had
gained too   They have grown in just these few
weeks I said how did that happen   Josie sighed
clucked her tongue said she didn't know was I so
sure they had gained   I said yes took them in
my hands and held them   She smiled the sweetest smile at me and put her arms around me
She said I could care for her any time I wanted to
that she was ready anytime   That sweet child
what a blessing at that moment   I kissed her
and held her tight   She said oh now dont pinch
me please but I did and she laughed and was like
a wonderful little child so full of spirit and energy
I said here darling put this on and held up Evies
dress with one hand but Josie kept hugging me
and didnt want to let me go   I said here now
Josie put on this dress I made for you and she did
but had a hard time getting into it   She has
gained a lot since I measured her last   She got
into it though and I said there there Josie honey
and turned her around to look into the mirror

She looked and it was like somebody hit her with something she seeing herself in that lovely dress she turned right back to me her eyes full of tears crying the poor child   She held out her arms to me sudden held them out quick   I said oh dont but was too late the dress my darling Evies dress split open   Split right open tore all the way down I said oh whats done now Josie   She said what what still holding out her arms so surprized she didnt know at first the dress had torn   Whats the matter she said what is it now   I said well the dress is torn   You tore Evies dress I dont think it can be mended now   She said what difference does that make here here and held out her arms still   I said Josie here now yourself just a minute   Josie started crying then and she got tangled up in the pieces of the dress and she ripped it some more tripped on it almost fell down Josie stop I said   She got mad then   Josie turned to me the hateful side of her nature   She threw the pieces of the dress on the floor and stamped on them   I had to be firm then   I have had to let Josie go   She was a blessing I want her back I miss her already but she was after all only a black girl inside my darling Evies dress

20 Today I did all the housework   Felt terible

21 I could not get out of bed today   David brought me my meals   He tried to make cornbread came out milky

23 I have been so sick

24 O I cant write in here today

30 Reverend Bayley has been here many times during
    the past days   He is a good man after all   I
    told him yes I have been wicked I have not been
    submissive enough to the will of Almighty God and
    that he is right about that   We must   We
    must submit   He told me how Jesus was tempted
    on the high mountain told me again how he was
    offered the whole world of earthly joy spread out
    before him if he would but say the words and he
    did not say them   Then Rev Bayley made such
    a beautiful prayer for me   I closed my eyes and
    saw the beautiful colors of the stained glass window
    in the church the purple red and yellow sky and the
    rising goodness of the face of Christ triumphant
    I wept and was comforted   Rev Bayley prayed
    rejoicing and he is helping so much   It seems
    I rise with Jesus when he is here   If only that
    could last then I would submit to the heavy will of
    Almighty God if only that could last

II

BELLOWS

December 5 It has been some time journal   Im sorry if youve been neglected but at least now I have come to open you up again   Are you stiff journal   I sure am

6 You understand I was too sick to write in here journal for a long time but Im better now   I will do better youll see   I have been out of bed a whole week now

7 We have boarders here now   David made me do it he thought it would be for the best   He took

me up to dear Evies room and we broke it all up
Moved the furniture about changed beds cleaned
out the closets everything about it changed for two
young ladies coming to board while they go to the
school   I almost could not bear it but David for
once was giving his all to be firm and I humored
him   Girls are Susan Balis and Elaine Ruskin
They came the next day and I felt homesick in my
own house   Found I liked the girls better than
I expected though   Am tired now will catch up
more later   I am glad to see you again journal

8 David got an old negro man named Hanks to do
the work here in the house while I was sick   He
is a good worker he proved that but of course old
and a man who cant wash things right get them
clean and keep up the house though he has been
a good cook Ill say that for him   But so old and
I dont like the way he looks at me   So today I
told David I would have to have another girl now
that I am up   I just couldnt walk around bumping into that old Hanks looking at me like that
David is glad to see me up and about   He smiled
and said well all right

9 Worked too hard today in bed again up down well
I feel like a yo yo sometimes journal   Is that
funny do you think   Journal am I witty
Smart thing you wont talk will you

10 Today David took me over to Dansville took me
to drive there where he is going in partnership on
another store   It is five miles David went slow
and had me bundled up tight   I didnt catch cold

It is a fine looking store nice people in and out
David has done well and I told him so

11 Back in bed today because of our drive but dont
need to be   David said just for caution   On
the way back just outside of Dansville one of the
horses acting up skittish bit in his teeth almost
David stopped and looked over the traces something
was rubbing wrong there and that fixed things all
right   When David got back up holding the reins
he looked up at the sky   There was a great whirling of clouds journal not black clouds but white yet
racing across the sky   Moving so smooth and
fast   The sunlight pouring through in places and
being shut off in other places   What it did to
the hills it made them speckled with shadows moving   Across from us beyond the fields was the
Collins range of hills and on top of them the out-
croppings of granite rock that have something in
them minerals or something that make them shine
sometimes   When the sunlight passed over them
and hit those rocks it was like diamonds to David
clear precious jewels he said   He has given up
a lot of deer hunting for me this fall   I said
David you must go deer hunting soon   He said
he would   Then he just pointed and looked at
me   Pointed and looked at me arm outstretched
The same sort of thing he did at Anson Ayers when
all the kin and people were there in the afternoon front yard   Pointed at the mountains and
sunlight so shiny in the cold distance   It is like
he is so amazed at me saying well cant you see
woman cant you see that how good it is   And I
nodded and said to him yes David it is fine

79

O David yes I can see all right   I can see you
have your world and it is all around you
You would even keep it in your clothes if I didnt
have them washed out for you   It is your delight
this world and you have your terms with it   I
can even see it must be hard for you not being able
to make me know how you feel I know about that
god knows   But David when you go to the lake
in your hat with the veil for the deerflys when you
sit behind your stand in the woods waiting for the
deer David you are satisfied   That is fine but
it is your kingdom not mine   When you want to
make me a native of that land which is yours I am
vexed   When you are so amazed I do not see it
as you do I am vexed   When you then get sorry
for me I am vexed   I see it David I see it
But I was not born to this land of yours my husband no I was not   I am in it with you standing
like a foreign person just like that who can see and
have some appreciation and smile and nod but who
is not native   What kingdom then what land for
me   You dont even know I want one David that
yours is not the only one there is   That is your
strength and Ill admit I could use some of it
O isnt it funny journal this is the same way I felt
when I was only shortly a bride married to my
early husband Edward   Nothing changes much
does it   Anyway David has been good to me
I must learn again to honor my husbands little
world and say yes it is fine David how beautiful

13 Worked yesterday didnt have time to write   A
lot to do before Christmas my boys will both be
home then   I am thinking a lot about David now

14 David brought a girl to help me   Told me he
was getting me this good girl   David what will
I ever do with you   She was a grumbly old
woman a hundred and five years of age if a day
All she did was stand sigh and look crossways at
me   We spent a total of about two minutes in
each others company   David says he will try
again but I know I am going to have to do it myself

15 For David mountains and swift clouds passing
through great bursts of sunlight old clothes and
mechanical work click click open and shut sweaty
and dirty shirts baggy pants big heavy boots guns
and fistfight talk men standing around laughing
crowds and fields and great large expanse   For
me a flower growing in a small place   O what
do we know about each other what do we know
about ourselves what is there for us now in this submission

16 I got a girl   Her name is Taylor   Thats her
first name Taylor   She is grinning all the time
and seems happy was very quick with the washing
today a trial day   I think she is going to be all
right   She is about twenty two or three

17 Church today   Snowed lightly last night the
town very pretty   Rev Bayley preached well
I think because of the snow and it such a bright
sunny day the light came in the church window so
full and strong   Jesus soar and take my spirit
with you   I sang well   Mrs Fanny Knap said
how good it was to hear me sing out again   No

sign of William Craig   I hear he is a heavy
drinker now stays home all the time no wonder but
I will not think on that anymore

18   The joyous season is coming to us rapidly   My
boys will be home   Elaine Ruskin and Susie
Balis will be out of school soon for holiday
Elaine Ruskin will leave for Dansville her home but
Susie Balis will stay here with us she has no parents
to share this time with   She is a fine pretty little
girl it will be good to have her here   I hope
Charlie behaves himself but no let me say that
better   I hope Charlie is well and strong enough
not to behave himself but will anyway   There

Same day   What a wonderful surprize today in the mail
My heart beat so fast   It is a book   A large
book sent to me and David by Ed   It is called
Sojurns in Europe and the Holy Land written by
Philemon Rudd PhD   A beautiful book just as
it is but when we opened it there was a black cloth
marker running down marking page 3   There
was a picture there   It showed the Savior of us
all standing with his hands held up smiling   He
is drawn very thin you can see through him as if
he is a spirit indeed   He stands towering over
the cities and the land of Europe   Behind him
is a wonderful sunrise   Well the whole thing is
just superb and my heart caught when I saw under
the foot of the Saviour Eds name and even more
Printed under the complete picture in little type
after the big line that says Following in the Masters
Footsteps is written Frontispiece by Ed my darling
boy   Well Ed maybe you are going get some-

where make something out of your talent for drawing after all who knows   He has written in pen
and ink Merry Christmas   O Christ whose figure
he has drawn for this book pull him to you my
son Ed

19 Stayed home all day reading Mr Philemon Rudds
book with Eds drawing in it   I declare Mr Rudd
is something else again   That man has been everywhere   I think he must have some kind of
motors in his legs   Good night what trips
I have set by the window and let the wind blow
and have been with Philemon Rudd all over the
continent of Europe   What a thrill

Same day Taylor is doing the washing   David had to go to
Dansville to see about the new store   I am per-
fectly all right here in my chair running all over
the world with Philemon Rudd   There is a simply splendid section about the ile of Corsica didnt
I tell you the man has been everywhere journal
Corsica is where Napoleon came from you know
Well Philemon Rudd talks all about that place
There are drawings but not by Ed his was up in
front and you cant have everything can you
These other drawings show the land harbors bays
and some mountains and such no real spiritual scene
like Eds   Corsica   It must be a wonderful
place   Warm there all the time I think   And
there are these castle like towers sticking up at the
entrance to the great bays that Philemon Rudd
says were built there because Corsica had a lot of
early Italians there who lived in different cities in
Italy and fought all the time even when they got

to Corsica   Thats why the Corsicans are so fierce
they have fought so much and been fought over all
the time   It is natural the great Napoleon should
come from there fighting and conquering all
There is a picture of him Napoleon as a young man
in his native land so proud and fierce   There is
a tune reproduced right in the book Beautiful
Ajaccio it is called   That is a city with a beautiful bay and with palm trees and blue sea   I
picked out the tune on the pianno and I seen these
proud people   They dress in black you see the
men in great black hats just walking along that
beautiful Ajaccio bay singing and taking their
proud ease   Corsica   Journal women there
when they have had all their children and they are
grown and gone such women are honored   They
sit proud too and fierce with nothing to grow inside
them any more but they dont care   They dont
let that finish them off   No indeed   They sit
in their long black dresses and them that are young
and do not yet know about life on this earth come
to them and ask   Under the palm trees by the
wide sea under the white clouds and the blue sky
are the black dressed women who will have no more
children but who are honored standing in their black
dresses flapping in the breeze as they abide there
empty and knowing while the young people come
asking saying what what and they tell them
Corsica   I think I would be happy there

20   Elaine Ruskin left today to go home for the holiday
Susie Balis has been so nice and helpful   She
has even worked some with Taylor   She is a little thing pert though   Has dark eyes and hair

almost jet black must wear glasses all the time
She has a nice disposition she and Taylor make a
pleasant pair   David brought in a fine spruce
We put it by the front window and will spruce it
up after supper   Spruce it up journal oh oh did
you hear that I am getting worse than David what
a wit

21 I have had a good day journal   David did a fine
job on the tree last night   He had great long
strips of cotton and he laid them on the branches
and wouldnt have our old dressings at all   Just
that cotton and of course the star at the top but
thats all   It looked funny the way he was doing
and I said David why be different what about the
candles and he said no candles be quiet   I said
David and he said hush   Then he kept right on
laying those cotton strips along the branches   I
thought oh David my Lord what a painful mess
you make   It took him three hours of solid poking before he was ready to look up from it
I just gave up my patience was gone Susie and I
played cards in the dining room   Then David
said well come and see   The way the cotton lies
its a clever thing I mean it   Up close its just
cotton step back a little and it is snow sitting on
the branches just like it does in the woods after a
heavy fall   David even weighted down the limbs
at the tips with a little lead so they droop so grace-
fully   It is something to see   I come into my
parlour and there it is a tree a spruce in my house
bearing its burden of beautiful snow   Cold heavy
beautiful snow white and frosty looking on the
burdened tree   It seems to me I can stand in

front of it so warm here in my house yet feel
the weight of the cold heavy wet snow how hard
and painful but so beautiful white and dazzling and
above it the star   Come home to me soon my
darling boys

22   Well journal I dont think I mentioned it but old
Mr Casper Mabee died on the 19th   His funeral
today all the swarm of Mabees there what a prog-
eny   Casper Mabee once owned most of the land
around this town and built himself up a shoe works
besides   It got this town going wasnt much here
before that   He kept up his mighty works until
at the age of ninety four he died finally   When
I saw him in the coffin it was for the first time since
I was a young woman here with my first husband
Edward   We met Mr Casper Mabee then at a
reception given for Edward and me his bride   He
was kind enough to come Mr Mabee   Said little
and took the fitting pose of the man who has done
much   Since then and my Lord journal since that
meeting how much has happened to me how we
measure by life and death like it was a ruler well
since then he just stayed home most of the time in
the big stone house he had at north end of town
Sometimes he went to the shoe works in a closed
buggy and sometimes you might see him sitting out
on his great porch wrapped in a afagan quilt but
that was all   Course he run all his enterprizes
anyhow his hand never left the helm   An industrious and frugal man journal as plain as day
Journal dont you think my words are getting better
Yes I am learning about this writing things down
journal a little dont you think   Makes me feel

good to get it down right   I hit old Casper Mabee off then an industrious and frugal man as plain as day thats him all right   Well anyway he died on the 19th and his funeral today   Rev Bayley preached and mentioned to me as the procession started to the Semetary that there had been some uproar   Seems in the will old Mr Mabee made it plain and definite there was to be no public funeral and no Semetary burial not at all   He just wanted somebody to herd all the relatives together and before the will was read and War broke out they was to stand before him in a plain box he wanted to be laid out in and each one pay their last respects privately and that was all   Then he wanted to be buried out in the woods   Had left a map showing where the place was   Way out in the country journal so Rev Bayley said in a woods part of his vast holdings of land   Well said Rev Bayley can you imagine getting all these people out there into the woods   Good night I said it would be a problem of transportation thats true   Im thankful it has not been necessary said Rev Bayley wiping his face with a handkerchief even though it is close to Christmas journal   I wanted to ask him what happened to change things but then Marshall Mabee the oldest boy he is about seventy or so now made a gesture and Rev Bayley had to move Now Marshal Mabee when he makes a gesture he is like some Corsican king like some Napoleon and you could tell Rev Bayley felt summoned and he went quick   I followed along with Mavis Grant and the rest rode to the Semetary with Mavis She knew all about it   Said they just broke that part of the will   Because all felt it just would

not do for Casper Mabee the man who came here
and made this town thrive and hum whose family
has since spread out all over the state and nation
whose holdings are so vast and whose stroke of the
pen did so much in his last years well he couldnt
just be buried in a hole out in the woods somewhere
So they put him in the family plot right on the
crest of a hill in the center of everything all the
headstone markers where all the Mabees he out-
lived lie   But they felt more had to be done too
Now one of them is named Julian   I dont know
him but he lives in the City and has built up
a great and thriving headstone business   Just
like his father that way   Well it seems he had
things all ready for the funeral and interment and
almost cried when they told him the old man
wanted to be laid to final rest in the woods under
some tree   But he cheered up when they broke
that part of the will   He had a set of wagons hed
brought with him and the headstone in one of them
and all the equipment for its placing in the others
I guess he cried hooray or something journal and
went to work there on the crest of their Semetary rise   The land there just rises up in a gentle
swelling there and there yesterday they laid to rest
Casper Mabee but there was some uneasiness about
it and I think I see what the old man meant   It
is the name you see   That headstone is simply
huge and of course the funeral service and all was
very grand the will being broken   The Mabees
did everything there was to be done such sumptuous
complete arrangements you never saw   Even had
a band playing dead march all the way out there
from the church   So many people all gathered

around   It was a clear day very blue sky and
everything stood out clear and sharp all the tombstones all the colors of black the people wore
But it all got uneasy   You see when it was over
there he was buried there on that gentle slope under
that great huge towering headstone   It has a
great square base with all sorts of carvings then a
shaft that sticks straight up about twenty feet in
the air   You know what I mean there is some
word for it I dont know   Well up it goes rising
high and then at the top a sort of head with cornice
carvings all over it   There it was towering above
him and all the others here in the Semetary his
tombstone and carved on the shaft written like this
                    MABEE
I dont know journal it made everyone feel uneasy
and one unprincipaled person even laughed
Anyway you had this feeling all the Mabees knew
they had gone a little too far in such splendor and
eloquence   Their name didnt fit too well such
behavior and headstone sculpture   People seen
then that old Casper Mabee knew what he was
about when he wanted to forgo all this and be
buried out in the woods   But it was certainly
too late then   You couldnt take him out of the
grave then and take down that great stone could
you   No   So there he is under that thing with
a rich acres worth of flowers and tributes and such
the dignity of his human death somehow set a little
cockeyed by it all   Mavis Grant and I stood
back while the relatives left   People then looked
at that thing again   MABEE it said shining
clear and sharp on that white rising thing lifting up
from the swell of the mound MABEE   Well it

was at that moment a little funny and people just came out with it and laughed   Me too I dont deny it   Then they stepped back a little and smiled and shook their heads in mirth then looked around them at all the graves about us and nobody laughed so much after that   I went over to my darling Evie and stayed there awhile the first time I have let myself come to her in many weeks

I said to her oh Evie my darling there is no maybe about it we will be together one day soon   Alice too with her sweet body new and fresh and the great wound closed though the blood will remain on the hands of William Craig forever   I said Evie my darling it wont be long before we are all together again   Then I left her to go catch up with Mavis and the others   We passed by that great tall upraised thing that people now seemed to be pretty glad to move away from   I was smiling when I come up to them   Mavis looked at me warmly and said time heals in spite of us and I said yes this is the first time I have come to my Evie and left her with a smile   She said well and she laughed mabee things are all for the best

I laughed too and left with them   O Evie my child forgive me but Christmas is near   I know you would want me to welcome them my sons home yes I will greet them for you darling Evie greet them with a smile

23 Tomorrow they will .be home   David had the pianno tuned   Joy to the World

24 They came this morning   My sons   Charlie and Ed my sons   O gentle Saviour and our

Father ours through you   They are such fine
young men   I thank you from the bottom of my
heart for giving them to me   I promise I will
not be unreasonable again but will bless you forever   You have been so good to me though I
have not always seen it   They are wonderful
my sons O let us praise you for our being forever

*25 Xmas
day* I gave David a watch a good heavy pocket watch
with a silver chain and a fine soft steady tick
It has a medal on the chain   David said whats
the medal for   I said to hang off your vest but-
ton if you ever wear your vest again   He said
O I see   David gave me a set of pens an ink-
stand and two books   One of them is Standard
Dictionary and the other is Colbert Moreheads
Correct English Usage   I said well David   He
said as long as I was going to write part of each
and every day away in you journal that I might as
well learn something while I was about it   I said
David thats a good idea and it is too journal why
not   Ed and Charlie gave David a hand tooled
shotgun with a gilded pheasant carved on one side
and a fox in a golden thicket inlaid on the other
side   It is 20 guage and David says what a
beauty and is so pleased   David gave Ed an eyeshade a green eyeshade and he gave Charlie a set
of armbands that keep your sleeves pulled up
David   He made them think a bit and blink a
few times at just an eyeshade and shirt bands
Said it was a good swap that garment wear for this
fine shotgun then give them the checks   Ed
thought it was funny Charlie didnt at first then he
seen the amount on the check he got and laughed

about it all then   Ed gave me a fine ladies walking cloak   It is beautiful and billows a lot of
fine cloth out behind me when I walk in it   I felt
like some princess in it some queen and Ed said
well thats what you are oh an old joke saying that
to mother but how my heart caught   Charlie
gave me a mahogany lap board and a set of paring
knives   I gave Charlie some mens striped shirts
and a new boater one with six sets of gayly colored
bands to slip over it   He seemed pleased enough
And I gave Ed a professional drawing desk David
sent for it from the City   It slants every which
way and will clamp down your paper while you
draw   Ed was pleased and stared at it with
much emotion   Poor little Susie Balis who is
here with us no presents to anyone from her
That is what I call stingy   I gave her some kid
mittens   Ed gave her a very nice book   All
she gave back was tears   She just cried and cried
and her dark eyes all full of tears making a runny
puddle and mess behind those shiny eyeglasses she
must wear   Poor girl she has no family and I
suppose our happiness upset her still it does look
like she could have wrapped up a box of matches
or something and given it to us   Well she is a
nice girl anyway   I dont have to worry about
Charlie with her he doesnt like Susie much   She
and Ed though seem to have a good time talking
to each other   Thats fine   Well we all went
to church   David broke down came too   Ed
walked in with Susie   Me with David and Charlie
We took our seats and when the hymns began it
seemed we were all in good voice and we sang   I
looked over my shoulder and the triumphant Jesus

soared up into the beautiful sky of his window   Ed
saw me looking at the window and he smiled and
nodded to me yes it was something all right   I felt
oh what can I say journal   I have tried to write
better each day and say things so they are more
apt but this beggars me journal   There is no
word for this in Davids dictionary he gave me
We sang and it seemed the old pew itself with me
and mine in it moved just moved forward like it
was on tracks and soared away with Jesus into the
bright colors of his sky drawn by horses of wonderful music oh tee hee journal what an imagination I have   Its silly I know but how thrilling
the thought of us all soaring up to heaven together
and this is what life is all about I think   God
bless us and god bless all the earth and let one day
every soul stand and praise God what a moment all
the people of the earth journal standing together
and singing praise   What pleasure that would
give dear Jesus who died for us so we could live
shed his blood upon the cross   Again Saviour
and Father for my sons and for this season of
sacred birth this one woman anyway gives you
thanks   No sign of William Craig not even at
Christmas   I would not have minded if he had
come for Christmas   He killed Alice my child
but I deny no man not even that one the birth of
Jesus   Well journal Jesus Christ is born again
and with him so are we

26 Ed upset today at dinner   Indigestion and bile
All this excitement and fine food he said and he
winked at Susie Balis then choked some more   A
good bed is the only cure he said and Susie Balis

blushed red as the stripes on the flag   I told Ed
go on upstairs and rest son and he smiled at me
and did

27   Ed feeling better still a little poorly though
Susie Balis running all over this house doing for
him

28   Ed feeling fine now   Looks real bright and his
eyes sparkle and shine   Today David took him
and Charlie deer hunting   I said Ed are you sure
son you feel strong enough   He said oh yes
David said it would be good for him he has had
too much City life   Charlie didnt say anything
he just kept looking at me sideways   I know he
and David have had some hard words   They are
words about me I think but more it seems worse
something in it about Ed too   Only two days ago
we were all so happy   I dont understand it

29   Well they brought home a deer   A doe   We
will have some good eating from it   But the head
wont make anything to mount thats the truth
David is mad about that   He didnt want no doe
killed anyway but when it was he saw it would
make a fine head to mount   Charlie shot the doe
but David and Ed got to her first   She was just
barely alive it seemed then she died when they
stepped up to her and lay still   David said all
right now lets get her up quick she may still be
alive get her up by her hind legs cut the throat
bleed her out quick so this head will be all right
and so she wont suffer   Then Charlie got there
A doe he said thats all then he put five bullets

into her head and face tearing up the flesh and bone with his heavy bullets out of that new repeating rifle David had borrowed from Ernest White for him   David said Charlie stood there bam bam bam bam bam cocking the action of that rifle fast as five bursts of light   Shot her head to pieces that doe   David wont speak to Charlie now Charlie just stands around smirking   It is like he is proud of what he has done   That poor sweet doe   Well we will have a lot of good eating from her head or no head

30   They are leaving today   They are not going to wait for the New Year   I heard them talking tonight upstairs   Talking loud and fast   I couldnt make out what they were saying   It was mostly Charlie and David arguing   I got my dressing gown and went upstairs and they said no this is mans business and there was nothing for it   I must go back downstairs   After that they talked low   I could not hear   Now today they are packing my boys are leaving going back to the City   Why are they going now   They dont have to not for two whole days yet   Whats wrong now journal whats wrong now

31   They left today   David wont say why   Just wanted to go get ready for work is all he will say

January 1   Today is the New Year   Went to service alone Came in with Mavis Grant who I met on the way No sign of William Craig   Mavis says he is just a recluse now   The singing sounded so harsh and loud   Just a week ago what an experience of joy

Now today I am sitting in about the same place as
last week except with nobody but Mavis with me
I turned during the singing to look at the window to
see the triumphant rising of Jesus in the colorful sky
and I seen him and nothing happened except I
thought well there he goes   A mean and bitter fall
on my part a hard thing to confess but it is the
truth   How can it all change so quick   What
torture

2 Taylor came back to work today   Pert thing
She asked about Susie thinking Susie might come
work with her keep her company as before   Susie
didnt   Her spirits so bright when the boys were
here are tarnished now   She just mopes about
Poor girl with no family just one uncle who lives
alone miles out in the country   Taylor did the
wash and cleaned some   I did what I could then
went to bed

3 David keeping something from me   Oh journal
I cant dig it out of him   David David

4 I got just frantic today   Knew something was
wrong so wrong I felt it squirm about inside me like
a dangerous birth something awful   I said David
you are not going out of this house today until you
tell your wife what is wrong here   I have to
know I just have to   I said David now you have
always been fair with me but you are not being fair
now   Tell me David tell me   David sighed
closed the front door came back in the house didnt
go to the store all morning   He stayed with me
and talked to me all morning   I am still upset
about Evie about so many things he said   I must

learn to be calm   It is not enough to be happy
the way I was at Christmas to pin everything on
one day a holiday like that there is always a let
down to be considered and the other days to face
I am making mountains out of mole hills I must be
calm said David chart a steady course and so on
What could I say to that except all right all right
I will try   I will try to believe nothing is wrong
I will

5   Ed left the professional drawing board I gave him
here left it on the back porch under a sheet   O
me journal that hurt

6   Taylor came for the wash   Wore a dress with a
little set of strawberries all over it   I said it was
a pretty dress   She laughed and said dont they
look good enough to eat though   Then she asked
me for more money   Said she needed it would be
glad to take on more work for it   I said I would
think about it and let her know next week   She
said I happen to know you gave those girls Calistra
and Josie raises and bonuses a lot how about me
then   I said Taylor well talk about it next week
Well neither Taylor or Josie are the girl that Calistra was   No asking for money or tearing up
dresses with her   I hope Calistra is just giddy
with happiness working for Mrs Nutt   She was
my favorite I have to admit it   I bet she makes
Mrs Nutt pay plenty too   O I dont care about
that mess

7   It has been a dull day raining all day   Wait a
minute where are my new books   It has been a
dull day, raining all day.   Does that look any

better to you journal   to you journal   Journal?   It dont to me   How long it has been since I sat behind a schooldesk   Opened up any schoolbook   Now here David has given me these two   I cant make much sense out of it it seems very complicated except of course spelling I was always good at that   But I might as well try Might as well try!

8   Cold, rainy, day.   I have not been out!   I have been sewing sheets and pillow cases, and, I have been looking through these infernal books!   Journal do you really care what you look like how I treat you   What do you think about it all journal eh?   O how I wish you could talk to me

9   Mended stockings all day.   Taylor hopping around, asked me again for more money, I said wait a while, Taylor!   There is a prayer meeting tonight at the church Church.   It has rained so much that if I can just get through all the puddles of water and streams running down the street I will go.   Now journal you tell me if thats a good sentence like the book says eh?   I will have to study harder or fool with these books no more.   Guess which one it is going to be

10   Good prayer meeting last night.   David smiles at me again now.   I have been good about trusting him and so he hands me my wonderful reward and I could spit.   What is it?   Journal what is it whats wrong now?

11   At prayer meeting the ladies were asked to start up a carpet sewing committee. Twice a week now we

will go to sew carpet for the Church.   Some of
the ladies are new; indeed, some of them I really
dont even know, not at all!   Hows that books

12   I got it out of Taylor she told me what is going on
finally finally journal   It was about the money
she trying to talk me into the raise and she said well
if your husband wins out then theyll all be back
here and you will need me in more ways than one
then   I said oh you think so Taylor and held my
tongue and breath   She said why yes   I said
well who do you think will win out   She said oh
your husband will Mr David will   I said why
She said because your boy Charlie aint much on
backbone   I said is that so well maybe youre
right how is David going to win   Then Taylor
said oh he will make Mr Charlie give in   I said
oh you really think so do you wondering fast and
furious give in to what but just asking quietly rais-
ing my eyebrows only a little   Oh yes said Taylor prattling on he will get Mr Ed back here all
right   Oh journal isnt it the servants who know
everything why hadnt I thought of Taylor before
Yes I said its just a question of when it will be
Taylor said well it cant be long now I almost ruined
one wash with those bloody cloths   I held myself
steady as a rock and said yes they are troublesome
arent they   Taylor said they sure are   I didnt
know how to go on with it then but she prattled
without my prodding and said how wild Charlie has
been to get Ed out of the house and back to the City
I sighed and kept saying yes yes and pretending to
pay little mind to what I made out I already
knew   But Mr David will let Mr Ed do what he
wants and you know he will want to come back here

I said of course he will and said oh Taylor you
are some spy   She grinned and switched her hips
like a little girl and said I know it how about my
raise   Well I had to stop then   I knew I would
have to wait until David got home   I said you
will have to hold off on that raise Taylor Im sorry
She said well wait a minute now and I said wait
a minute yourself gave her a pinch on her bottom
maybe a little harder than I meant to and said I
just might have to get myself another girl   She
said well shed wait another week then   When
David comes home I will be waiting for him

13   David when he got home looked just as grim as me
here waiting for him   I told him what Taylor
had let slip and he said yes yes its true enough shes
right   Both boys will be here tonight on the train
I said David   He flared up then saying you
will just have to wait until then there are things
about it I dont know yet   I nashed my teeth
journal and waited   David went to meet the train
wouldnt let me go with him   They all come into
the house together David Charlie and Ed   My
three together David quiet and calm and pinkfaced
but Charlie chin up mad at the world just spoiling
to defy me his mother any way he could and then
Ed   O how strange he looked   Pale and worn
but his eyes shining and sparkling and his complek-
tion flushed and bright I said Ed honey   He said
hello there mother how are you   I said Ed you
left your drawing board here on the back porch dont
you want it   He said yes he knew about that said
he also knew hed be back here soon enough to put
it to some use and he smiled a weak and thin smile

but his eyes danced and shined they were bright as
stars   Charlie swore then and cursed horribly and
David looked at him deadly and just whispered
none of that and Charlie shut up   I stood there
a minute and they stood there a minute and I
smiled at my men and didnt know what to say to
them at all for a minute until Ed put down his bag
and there was a tip of a cloth sticking out of his
coat pocket and part of it was red   Well whats
for dinner said Ed reaching out to give me a peck
on the cheek   His breath smelled bad and I
reached into his pocket caught the tip of the cloth
a pulled it out   It was a bloody handkerchief a
mess wet and sticky   I said nothing is for dinner
until you tell me what all this means   So they
told me it seems journal Ed has been sick for months
He was sick all the time I was in the City and
he was sick during the wonderful Christmas we had
together more than just excitement and bile and
Susie Balis all around him   Charlie had wanted
him to go into the hospital in the City but Ed didnt
want to do it and David had to settle the matter by
telling Ed of course he could come home   Men
Not until I held the handkerchief in my hand would
they tell me and even then because I said no dinner
no nothing nobody goes another inch into this house
until I know all so tell me the rest of it   They did
then   Ed has had a hemerage of the lungs   O
what a shock to me   My precious boy   God
help me

Same day   We had dinner   They went on to bed   I
washed out Eds handkerchiefs in the sink   A
mess I got it all over my hands

Same day
very late Ed will be home now for some time   Charlie too
He gave up his job and room at the boarding house
There will be a lot more work to do now   Our
family together again is so much bigger   Taylor
is a good girl after all   She says all right to extra
work I see you are in trouble   I may give her that
raise after all

14 Sunday today went to Church alone   Could not
bear hardly to speak to anyone   There was some
snow but grey and cloudy too   Everything
seemed so slow and dull grey and colorless   My
wonderful window so drab   Rev Bayley spoke on
keeping the faith the torch aflame but my heart did
not rise the way it should have   I sat there a
lump of clay Ed my darling boy   I prayed and
prayed hard as I could not listening to Rev Bayley
I just couldnt I prayed and prayed   Then he
called for the hymn it was one I didnt know didnt
remember   I found it in the hymnal everyone
started in but my voice was not good so I just
watched the lines of the first verse go by as they
sang   They were this

> Slowly, by thy Hand Unfurled
> Down upon the weary world
> Falls the darkness   O how still
> Is the working of thy Will

I shivered   I shivered all over   I put the
hymnal down and left the Church   They was still
singing but I left shivering my hands and fingers
and toes cold as ice and snow

16 Had to let Elaine Ruskin go find another room
somewhere I think she is in with Mrs Fanny Knap
now   Ed is in her and Susies room which was
Evies best room in the house with the most morning
sunlight   The light my poor Evie loved so
Susie was so upset at the thought of leaving   She
said now that this trouble was upon Ed and upon us
she wanted to help   I felt like saying no but
David said well you can have the back downstairs
bedroom if you want it and there she is now   She
is a sweet girl poor thing no family   Its all right
with me

17 What a lot of work getting this house going again
Taylor doing all right so far   Lots to do no time
much to write journal sorry but thats the way it is
I am busy busy

18 Busy busy

21 Not been able to write for several days Im sorry
Ed seems to be improving   Dr Rudge says so
anyway   Charlie has gone to work in Sam Fow-
lers dry goods store

27 Got the upstairs floors waxed all but the hallway

28 Ed sound asleep this morning looked like he would
stay that way til noon   Susie said if you are going
to Church let me go with you   I said all right but
there are others things first   She came with me to
Hubbards hill to get some evergreen   Walked
with me to the Semetray no Cemetary and when I

laid some on Alices grave she asked me about her
Wants to know all about the family you see   Well
I told her unblushing how my sweet Alice my first
child by Edward was taken advantage of first by a
fly by night sweetheart and then in her own confused and unhappy state of mind let herself lay
down under the knife of William Craig and be
butchered   Susie took my hand then   She has
a generous nature or at least so she would have you
think   Went on to Church   Susie cant sing at
all   Just swallows and squeaks a little and holds
the hymnal so I cant see it

31   Ed is getting quite strong with all the work we are
doing for him   O how I pray he may get his
health back there is nothing I would not do   Susie
is with him every minute she can get out of school
but I do not know what it will all amount to   Ed
is sick it seems to me sort of foolish   But if she
can be any comfort to him I shall have nothing to
say   Mavis Grant says she thinks Susie came
here thinking to get him or Charlie either one but I
said no I cant believe that   How could she know
they would be home not in the City

February 1   When Ed come he wanted his drawing board moved
into the room with him   He has been trying to
use it and has a good deal drawing a lot   David
keeps him supplied with ink and pens from the store
and today Charlie brought him a lot of canvas and
some paints   He hasnt started in on that yet today just the drawings   Such strange things
All these cats and dogs and kangaroos and crocka-
diles and hedgehogs even a leopard all standing up

104

dressed walking around like people   Some of
them are women and its embarassing the things he
has them doing   I say nothing about it though
the poor boy   Only today I did remark I thought
it was a dangerous waste of energy to draw so many
pictures now and to think about painting and all
He smiled so pale and said oh mother to paint a
picture even a bad one is the greatest thing any human can do   I said well Ed that may be but you
want to save yourself son   He looked at a drawing he was doing it was a hedgehog riding a bicycle
and he held it up and said yes maybe but save myself for what   I tried to laugh said well for me if
nothing else   Ed smiled put down the drawing
and said he would have to think that over for awhile
Then he got up out of bed pushing his drawing
board away and started fooling with the paints
I said now Ed honey but then Susie was at the door
can I come in and Ed said Susie come in you can
help me with these paints and the canvas   That
was plain enough goodbye for me journal wasnt it

2 Worked hard all day today   Going to Church tonight to sew carpet

3 Ed feels much better and took Susie to ride this evening even though we know he shouldnt have   I
   walked down to the Cemetary wait a minute yes
   thats right Cemetary after sunset   It was cold
   but I felt I must go I was so lonly lonely   I felt
   so sensitive   To think I had to walk while they
   went to ride never thinking of mother   It was
   quite dark when I got there and wrapped my new
   ladies cloak around me tight found my old weeping

place under the Raymond Wingate marble angel
with outspread wings and I just knelt down there
and told my darlings taken from me how I felt all
about it how terible it was to live without them
How no one cared for mother as they used to
Then journal I sort of stopped that and wondered
what I looked like there under the wings of the angel
and if we could see ourselves I thought what am I
doing   I thought no one cares for mother includ-
ing me   This is no way to behave I thought
I dont think I would like you either mother get up
and I did and started back trying to get hold of
myself as David says I must but on the way I met
Ed and Susie come in the trap to get me   David
sent them they met me at the State House just as
the clock struck nine said get in   I wanted to
but I didnt I said no thank you I am walking for
my health let me keep mine please and went on
home   They drove behind a little   I could even
hear them whispering through the horseclops and
the rattles of the trap   Sounded like flies buzzing
I am tired now ready to sleep   A bad day but it
has done me good somehow

4   Ed has gone with David to Lake Madison to hunt
    and make a winter camp for two days   He cer-
    tainly seems strong but who can say   I am so
    anxious about him   He and Susie got engaged be-
    fore he left even though theyve known each other so
    short a time   Seems desperate to me

5   Journal you never in your life saw such things as Ed
    is drawing   I went into his room to clean when
    he was on the porch with Susie and looked at some
    he has never showed me before   These animals

are so like people its frightening   There is a frog
all dressed up in tie and tails and a crockadile in a
bathing suit and a kangaroo in a ladies dress but
the kangaroo has a great large womans bosum they
stick right out over her bodice   The frog is cover-
ing his eyes the crockadile is laughing and showing
great teeth and with the kangaroo hopping after the
frog   They are lifelike I will say that anyway

6 Well I did laugh   Today I was in Eds room
cleaning again and Taylor came in   She saw some
of those drawings before I could set them down
She said Lord God whats that   I said well its art
Taylor have yourself a look   She did began to
giggle   Got quite excited Taylor did   I never
seen anything to beat this have you she said   I
said no what do you think about them   I think
they are wicked said Taylor with a grin   Is that
all I said   She said no I think they are a little
mixed up   I said what do you mean   She held
up several of the drawings all the animals dressed
and undressed chasing each other and running from
each other squatting down doing shocking things
Taylor held them up and said your boy has got to
make up his mind if he is a people drawing animals
or an animal drawing people   I said Taylor thats
a fact   We both laughed then   Taylor is a
smart trick journal you know that

7 Susie just comes home from school and hangs about
She is so miserable without Ed on his camping trip
I said buck up girl you have to face life better than
this   She got very upset   Went to her room
and locked the door

8   Ed will be back tomorrow   Charlie cant help it I
guess but I never thought he would talk to me the
way he does these days   Just worry over Ed I
suppose   Still even though I try to understand I
just dont like it   When I pass Taylor in the
kitchen now she winks at me and says Kangaroo or
woman which is it   Man or frog which is it and
did we giggle almost laugh out loud   Without
some sense of humor journal humans would not last
one day would they

9   Ed came home today with David looking fine
Rosy cheeks a grin on his face   Poor David he
thinks all you to cure a boy of lung hemerage is take
him deer hunting let the cold redden his cheeks
Dr Rudge was here says Ed is better   That pitiful Susie like a little spaniel wagging her tail
Such trouble with Charlie   He came in drunk
before dinner all his nice clothes dirty his face filthy
where he must have fallen down somewheres   He
wanted to take Ed back out deer hunting or something   David had to be firm with him   Poor
Charlie so unhappy still it is a good thing David is
here controling him   It is so hard to write this
but I have become afraid of my son Charlie   I
say Charlie son whats bothering you so these days
and he bites his lip taps his foot and wont answer
He looks at me now with hatred   Thats what it
is I see it   O Charlie why

10   Ed has gone back to his drawing again   He staid
inside all day working   I went up to see but he
didnt want me to come in   Susie didnt go to
school   She staid with him in there

11 Ed not well today   Of course he took cold on that
foolish trip   His coughing began again today it
makes me tremble it is so deep you can hear it all
over the house like something tearing   I am so
afraid he is not going to get over it   The Temperence people are on a raid hope they may do something this time

12 David had to leave today to go see about his store
in Dansville   Charlie gets up goes on to work
without a word to me comes home dresses and goes
out at night to the saloon probably   I dont know
when he comes home

13 My house such an uneasy place   I just had to get
out today I went for a long walk   Saw Mrs
Phiney who told me Mavis told her William Craig
is drinking himself into his grave   Well journal
you know what I think about that do you very much
blame me

14 Ed up today   He has taken Susie his darling
bride to be out to a dance here in town   Can you
imagine   How I did feel to have him go knowing
he is not well enough   Susie doesnt care she has
no more sense than to dance him to death

15 Went to Temperence meeting this afternoon   It
was quite an affair I think those people really do
mean to do something powerful   How wonderful
that would be

16 David back today   I wonder if he has any idea
how he has changed from what he was the first
weeks after Evies death such a short time ago

Then he was so kind and thoughtful of me now he finds fault with what I do   Susie wants to quit school and stay with Ed   David thinks thats fine

17   Had some company to dinner   Everything went wrong   Makes me almost sick

18   What a sad lonely day   O that my Evie was here to talk to me   God help me to endure these trials I just have to put up with Susie I knew it was a mistake letting her stay here but didnt say anything my error   She is so thoughtless rushing about not looking what she is doing   Perhaps I ought to overlook more things than I do though after all she has no family no mother to advise her There I go again mother mother mother

19   Another Temperence meeting tonight   We are having warm pleasant weather like April

20   Well the raid did not work right it seems   Because of the town political control the Temperence people are defeated   What a sadness has come over all the hearts of all good Temperence workers and the cry goes out what shall we do now

21   Have felt bad all day   Susie is in Eds room all the time helping him paint   Thats what they say and maybe so but even if thats what theyre doing in there I tell you a sick man cant spend all that time painting away all day with Susie and expect to get much better   They are up there all the time and I can say nothing   David thinks it is just the ticket   What a fool David you are

Such a blind thing   It makes me harden my
heart against you so   Why cant you see anything
David

22   A group of ladies met today   Mrs Nutt called us
together to join up with the Temperence people
She of course taking over high and mighty   She
didnt like it much me being there but I came with
so many others she had to accept me with the rest
of them   So we have formed a new Temperence
Society   Busy now trying to get organized and
think up a good name   Something bold is what
we want   We mean to see what we can do to stop
the rum traffic and will hold prayer meetings first
for awhile and have testimonial evenings   Soon
we hope we will have strength from on high and the
numbers here to go and plead with and pray with
every rum seller here that they may stop this terible sin   Whats a good name for this mission journal cant you think one up for me to put in to them

24   Journal this painting thing is awful   Today I
made them let me in   There stands Ed brush in
hand poor pitiful Susie sitting on his bed combing
her hair   Ed looked about so wildly   Journal
he and Susie have stitched all that canvas together
tacked it all up on the wall and it reaches side to
side the whole length of the room   Journal there
is nothing human on that thing   These long
big shapes bumping into each other   Circles all
around split and jagged cracked like a soda cracker
Crazy bright colors and great thick black lines
here and there   I was just speechless   Ed said
well it isnt finished maybe it never will be either

I thought that would be a good thing but all I said
was oh   Then Ed didnt answer just stared at
that thing   And the room journal the room
Evies lovely sunlight bedroom it is now like some
hotbox about to blow up   Is that the way paint-
ers are I cant believe it   When Ed was a little
boy and Edward his father still alive we gave him
some paper and pens to draw with because it pleased
him and he would be quiet happy to stop his fussing
and play quietly with them   Now my Lord
If we had only know what it would lead to   If
artists and so on are this way journal it just isnt
right   My poor boy just standing there staring
with something God knows what deviling him boiling around in him   How I hate that   It is
womanish   It is the way an unhappy woman
carries her first baby like that you know   It is
no way for any man to be   I hate it

25   Went to Church tonight to sew carpet   David
     says I shouldn't do both carpet and temperence at
     the same time but I will as long as I can hold up
     God in heaven knows it occupies my mind   Im
     tired out now and think I can sleep

26   Journal I think I had my first dream tonight in
     a long time   I dont remember what it was just
     that I had one   First time in so long   I
     wonder what it was   Cant remember

27   Waxed all downstairs today   So tired but felt
     good   Tonight just now as I sat here starting to
     write some wind journal come in under the window
     which is cracked a little   It blew out my lace

curtains a bit in a delicate movement in a swirl
Out the window clouds sailed away from the moon
and it shone through on me so bright   What can
I say foolish thing that I am but I felt here with
pen in hand I felt like a woman again with lace
curtains and a little wind and moonlight   My
journal we have become friends late in life havent
we   So much I could tell you journal my good
friend   But it is too late now besides I would
write all ten fingers to the bone   Well good night
journal you are a good friend to me I appreciate it
more than I say

28 Nobody slept last night   Ed much worse   I
knew it dear God I knew it

29 Dr Rudge here yesterday and today   Put Ed in
other upstairs bedroom   Mad at me for letting
him stay in that close room painting   What
could I do   Susie hysterikal most of the time
O that girl

March 3 Ed is very sick taken with pneumonia   We
feared he would not live through the day   What
shocks what blows

4 A little better today but so sick

5 About the same   Coughs so much a pan full today

6 Mass Temperence meeting tonight I wont be able
to go because of Ed cant leave him   Mavis says
they still cant get the right name one bold enough
maybe they will chose it tonight

7   Ed much worse   David staid up all night with
    him   No staid spelled stayed   Ed was deliri-
    ous   This morning when I went in David come
    out of the room after all night vigil his face pink
    and ruddy him smiling rubbing his hands saying
    well we got through that one all right old girl and
    I could have killed him   David would feel he
    had to be cheerful in hell   He would just hold
    his hand right out for the Devil to pop a burning
    coal in   I know Ed must have raved all night
    because he has today and wont stop   My Lord
    the things he says   David just smiles and nods
    his head as if that is what he has expected in
    earthly life all along   What kind of bloodless
    thing are you husband of mine

8   Worse and worse   This house going crazy
    You cant go anywhere in it without hearing poor
    Ed talking to himself just raving my darling
    I could stand Susie no longer   Today David took
    her to board with Mrs Fanny Knap

9   Charlie screamed at me today   My son raised his
    hand to his mother now in this dredful crisis   I
    made David see to him   He will not be allowed
    in this house for awhile   Dredful spelled dreadful

10 I thought Ed was dying tonight   Susie came over
    and I allowed her in   Ed did not seem to know
    her asked who she was   She was all right for
    awhile then she started crying   I said plain to
    her Susie be quiet do you want to kill him   She
    said no no no and ran out of the house

12 How many days now journal I am losing count
David and I both sat up last night   David not
so cheerful now   I fear Ed will never get up from
this terible sickness   He is rational now

13 Long talk with Dr Rudge   He says Ed may get
around the house again if he lives but the sickness
has weakened his lungs and he can never be well
Sooner or later he must go   My heart how it
aches   Thank God for Taylor   That pert and
smart little girl is doing everything here now
And not a word about her raise   One blessing
after all one I didnt expect the way she talked
before

14 Today Ed heard me and Taylor go into his painting
room   We havent touched it since he collapsed
Just left it the way it was the door locked his drawings all over on the floor and everywhere   Two
bedsheets hung up over the canvas that stretches
over one wall   From his bed in the other room the
poor boy cried no leave it alone in there leave it
alone   We did but not before we seen it what he
has done   Taylor unhooked the bedsheets and
they fell to the floor and there it was in the light of
our two lamps held up that stitched together canvas
filling the whole wall   We stood feet deep in the
drawings littered about and looked up at it
Journal what has happened to my poor boy he has
forsaken God entirely I fear   All the shapes are
I guess finished now because you can see what they
are in a fashion   Great lumps and whirling circles splitting open bumping into each other some

black as night coming out of others gayly colored
God knows they dont look like soda crackers now
And fire   Everything there is on fire lumps circles and black things emerging out   Flames all
over everything you can see them burning some
straight up like a house or barn burns others slant-
ing and beginning to burn like a brush fire just
touched by the breeze ready to flare   That is the
background   Journal in front of this great waste
of misery of flame and horror are the animals again
But this time they are as big as people in life
and color   Same size as Taylor and me standing
in front of them and they are awfully real you hold
your breath   Then when you see what is happening you want to hold hand over eye and call upon
the hosts of heaven to come down and take that
thing into hell where it belongs   The crokadile
is there bigger and standing up straight   Journal
he holds a Bible his both hands holds it up reading
from it and staring up in the air and journal he is
a man has a mans body because you can see it
drawn painted right there in front of you   His
physical mans male member it is long and stretched
way out hard and to it with a piece of rope is tied a
long sword   I couldnt believe my eyes   Even
Taylor who doesnt faze so easy she gasped
Then behind the crockadile is the frog   He is
down   He is dead   I guess killed because he
lies there with a walking cane stuck into his heart
but his face is smiling though and his frogs arms
and legs all flopped out loose   Then at the feet
of the male crokadile is the kangaroo a woman with
a dress all tangled up big long paws sticking out
the edges and fringes of the dress burning ready to

flare   She is bent over chewing on her exposed
bosum biting her own nipples like a human womans
and in her pouch and sack there is the hedgehog
playing with a yo yo while the kangaroo is rolling
around like that at the foot of the crokadile   I
heard Ed crying get out get out of there leave it
alone get out of there and I said come on Taylor
lets go and whoo Taylor was already out the door
I called to Ed in a soothing voice yes honey well
leave it just like it is and I started to close the
door but looked back   You have to be at a distance and a slant to see the tears   Ed painted
them so they shine when you step away   The
crokadile holds the Bible looking up to heaven
His great teeth sticking out of his mouth in that
awful grin and his male body member sticking out
with the sword tied to it and then down from his
eyes come the tears   They shine like pearls
When I got into Eds room he was trying to breathe
Hed had a spasm couldnt make it over the side of
the bed to hit his pan and had bloodied his pillow

17   Couldnt go to Church of course   Been home all
day today Sunday   All this day I have been trying to say to God thy will be done   I dont know
how I can do it   I will of course though but it
is so hard to lose my noble boy even if his mind
has become diseased by painting   He is my son
Ed none the less

18   Ed has rallied a little bit   He is sleeping sound
now I let Susie go up there with him   Taylor
doing almost everything for me now   I am about
played out

19   Got hold of myself today scrubbed the hallway walls upstairs

20   Susie left today   For good   Ed told her not to come back told her himself   O how I wish I had loved Susie better   Poor girl she has no one to advise her   I made allowances for that didnt I journal   But she was too hard on Ed and he finally seen that it couldnt go on   I know I have been a little jealous I know that   But it seemed so foolish for her a poor girl wanting to marry a dying boy   Yet perhaps I would have done the same   Anyhow shes gone

21   Last night Charlie tried to break into the house I heard him and met him on the steps   I said no no you will not see Ed   I called David Charlie screamed awful things about saving Ed about protecting him before hes dead crazy awful things and he cursed horibly   David hit him Then Charlie cried like a little boy and ran away Ed slept through it all praise God   When will this end O Saviour

22   Swept out the basement soaked it down with buckets of water but overtaxed myself had to sit on the steps and call help to Taylor   What will happen now I am so weak

26   Have been in bed all this time   Dr Rudge made me   Taylor has taken over helped so much worked herself to the nub without a word   Ed has slept a lot   O God I get up tomorrow

27   David made me go out of doors   First time I
have been out of the house in so long   I went
to Temperence meeting

28   Did a little work today   Ed sleeping a lot still

31   David made me go to Church today   Everyone
so kind   I wish they would look the other way
when I come in   I am heartily sick of this now
and I dont care one way or the other about what
they have to say

April 1   Today the doorbell rung   I stripped off my apron
went to answer   Opened the door and found
Charlie there standing on the porch and with him
dear merciful heaven stood William Craig   He
was shaking and trembleing and when I opened the
door he backed away quick   Charlie took him
by the arm dragged him back to the door and said
mother we want to talk to you   I yelled David
David at the top of my voice though of course he
was at the store and couldnt hear me   Charlie
tried to get in but Taylor come running up   William Craig just stood muttering to himself and
shaking   He is a great wreck of a man now
thanks to the justice of God   Charlie meant to
get in the house talk to me see Ed and bring that
awful man in with him   I put both my arms
weak as they are out across the door journal and
kept yelling   Taylor came up pushed me from
the behind for support that blessed girl   Then
suddenly Charlie stopped trying to get in just stood
there staring over my shoulder   I turned around

There was Ed   Standing on the stairs holding on
to the bannister   He said hello Charlie and Charlie said wildly Hello Ed listen Ive come here to save
you and then Ed tried to smile but he coughed like
a tearing of cloth and the blood spurted out at us
from his poor mouth   Charlie let out a yelp then
and run to get Dr Rudge who is with Ed now
William Craig vanished quick   David got home
He told Charlie if he tries to get in here again without our sayso he is going to shoot him with the gun
they gave him for Christmas and David means it
too   Charlie in the name of the Lord what are
you trying to do to us

2 Ed in a desperate way   No rest for anyone now

3 Ed rallied   He is sleeping again   Today I
looked out in the street and seen Charlie standing
out there by the picket fence with Susie   My
hands shake so bad these days I cant sew cant
hardly write

4 Spring again journal   Wouldnt you know Almighty God would have it come forth in such glory
this year   And I am supposed to give thanks for
it journal   Ed is hanging by a thread   Journal
is that a rime   I guess so

5 Ed had soup two oyseters today   He asked about
his drawings and painting I said son they are just
where you left them dont fret about them   He
smiled and whispered I was right he didnt think
there would be anybody knocking down the doors
to get in and see them   He is so thin now and

pale   A skeleton his suffering is using him up
Only that frail willpower of his seems to be left
But he hangs on I give him that as I gave this world
a brave son in the first place

6   Painted the kitchen floor today

7   Temperence meeting tonight   Did not go to
Church   Taylor came today I said Taylor its
Sunday you dont have to be here   She said just
mumbling thats all right I mean to help you all I
can   What a surprize she is not a word about
that raise   I thought she was so pert and selfish
But no there is some degree of great feeling too in
this once so sassy girl

8   Eds mouth and throat in terible condition   Dr
Rudge had to hold his tongue and scrape it   Can
eat but little   Trying to regulate this house again

9   So much raving today thought it would never end
It was a lovely day though O God you made a beautiful one this time didnt you

10   Charlie died this morning   Another beautiful day

11   I have made a beautiful wreath for Charlie

12   Charlies funeral today   Charlie Robinson that is
The blacksmith here for many many years   As a
little girl I used to go watch him so strong pound
out the hot metal and melt it down in his forge with
his bellows lay it on the anvil and pound it into
shape with the big hammer that had a sharp pointed

end on one side and a blunt heavy end on the other
Old Charlie Robinson served this town well all these
years   Journal did you think I meant my son
Charlie who hates his mother these days   Did I
fool you journal

13   Clouds in the sky so white they have no cares
I had strange dizzy spell today   Fell going down
steps   Taylor came picked me up held me in her
strong young arms   Thought I had sprained my
ankle but no it is all right   Ed hemeraged last
night again   Bled a lot like a pig

14   Felt I had to go to Church today   My ankle hurt
but I went anyway   Reverend Bayley talked
about the sparrows that are not gone without notice
I thought Ed if you could just turn into a spar-
row and just quick skit out from under it all and
fly away   Reverend Bayley talked then about
the mill of the gods   Oh ha ha

15   Tried to find out about carpet sewing at the Church
when they meet now but it seems they have all gone
to join the Temperence work nobody cares about
sewing carpet now

16   Today Eds room empty   He was trying to get
into his old room and his painting had collapsed on
the floor   I do not know how much more I can
stand   Made up a cot in his room will stay with
him now until the end

17   O it is me who will die first   Last night I woke
up I knew somebody was in the room with us

It was Charlie   He was bending over the bed
trying to wake Ed up   My yelling sent him
jumping out the window where he slid down over
the shingles of the porch roof to the ground and was
gone   O my God   Journal I can remember
Charlie doing that clambering out that same window when he was a little boy and Ed too after him
laughing   Insanity this life

18   When Dr Rudge left today Ed could not get out of
his bed   I got him up and onto my cot   Made
his bed up fresh for him   When I got him back
into it he could hardly breathe   He whispered
how good and clean the bed smelled like sweet soap
How I love to get into a clean bed he said   I
guess thats another rime journal   3 of them even
bed said Ed   I said yes son you will always
have your bed that is clean and fresh as long as I
am here to care for you   Then he rested   I
watched him   When he woke up again I knew
what I had to do and did I talked to him very
plainly   I told him I feared he did not have long
to live   I asked if there was anything at all he
wanted to say to me   He said no he didnt think
so   I said you know what I mean Ed what I pine
to hear   He looked at me and then he said yes
well I am trying to trust in Jesus hows that
Made me so relieved   I said oh Ed are you sure
He said well I will put my trust in the Jesus
in that stained glass window at the Church hows
that   I said oh wonderful son   That is a fine
likeness of our Lord   Then he got nervous as
much as he could in that wasted condition   He
said where is Charlie   I said in town   He said

where is Susie   I said not here do you want me
to send for her   He said no it would do no good
she is in school again isnt she   I said yes
Then he said where is David my step father   I
said at the store   Then poor Ed wanted to get up
out of the bed go to the store and do a days work
for David   He was not rational   He kept saying maybe if he started right now by the end of the
day he could make a dollar   I have made no
money since before Christmas he said and then he
shuddered and coughed but no blood then   I said
go to sleep Ed   I have had another bed made up
in my room downstairs   We might be more comfortable there I think   I could use the extra and
Ed could sleep in my bed

19   Evie   Alice   My lost darlings   Brush your
hair and put on your prettiest dress   Sit on a
star and hold out your dear arms for Ed

20   Ed suffered horibly last night   I did not sleep
the cot too hard   This morning David said all
right then and went up to persuade Ed to move
down to my room   So much more comfortable
there   So much easier to manage everything
Ed did not say much at first but after awhile sighed
and consented   How silly I am it seemed for a
moment when we got him down here to me that
this solved everything   He is here now asleep
Dont scratch pen you will wake him up

21   How I did pity my poor boy leaving his rooms upstairs knowing what it must probably mean
Those rooms where he painted and where he suffered

so   How many hours he lay there alone clinging to life no doubt pleading to his heavenly father for some breath   There he must have give up all hope and I trust his heart to Jesus   I will take care of him in my room again tonight

22   Ed going oh journal you can see it happening you can watch if you had eyes you would see it as I must now

23   He doesnt breathe more than a grub in the dust But he still lives   I do not breathe more than a grub in the dust either journal   I still live too

Same day   My darling is gone   Died this evening quarter past ten   I hope I shall never pass through such another time   Reverend Bayley came in to pray the evening away with him   Ed seemed to be choking to death just after eight oclock   I told him his sister Alice and dear Evie were waiting for him they would surely be there   That I would be coming soon   He put up his hand touched my arm with his fingers a touch light as a moths wings and said well all right mother   I asked him if he could trust in Jesus   He said well why not we have always been good buddies   Rev Bayley seen then that he was raving and took no offense as I trust Jesus didnt either   From then on he just rolled his eyes my noble son Ed until at quarter past ten the fatal moment came upon him
He whispered something like I will do more just give me better paint then like the jump of a horse he thrashed lay back frowned once and was gone
Now Journal it is hard let me never try to write

125

down just how hard but Journal I know our Redeemer is there and there in his strong arms is my son   Journal I know as I know I have bones and blood that Ed is now with his loved ones free from all pain and no more sickness there   No long nights of wakefulness dear Journal   No more suffering Journal I inscribe it here hard as I can press the pen   My darling boy lives in heaven resting now   That I inscribe Journal that I inscribe   Almighty God do not forsake me

26   Here I am at the Cemetary   Taylor is with me Stands holding the flowers we will in awhile place on the graves of my three children   The wind blows teribly but I am sitting under the protection of the Raymond Wingate black marble angel   These great wings stop the wind   With this protection now as the dusk comes on me and mine here under the earth Journal I can write a little bit   I am sort of hunched up here and have my ladies walking cloak on it is warm I have the long flaps tucked around my waist   It is pretty cold mostly windy but still right cold for Aprils end Dusk is down on us as I said but there is some last sunlight on the grass that is nicely cut here It makes grass that shiny green like when there will be a storm   There are lots of clouds moving fast in the sky but there seems to be no rain in them A cloud with no rain thats me Journal what I feel like   Taylor has on a floppy hat   She holds it with one hand some of the flowers with the other while the wind blows upon her too   She just waits for me   Such a fine girl she has been through it all Taylor

Journal they all came again   My brother Henry
all the others   The ladies of the town   Anson
Ayers and the relatives all of them how I wished
they had not come just stayed home what need had
I of them this third time   In the parlour again
all the footsteps and the hush   In the same place
where my darling Evie only oh how long it is
Journal let me look   Oh only 11 months ago give
or take a few days   Since then that short time
now Ed is laid here in the same place   From his
coffin the face gleamed so white and pale a saint
thats what my poor boy looked like I dont care
what he painted on that canvas   Anyway nobody
but me and Taylor has seen that   I locked the
door put the bedsheet back over it too   Wont give
up the key not even to David   11 months how
short a time little did I think noble Ed would have
to follow in sweet Evies footsteps so soon   How
little we know what God has in store for us   O
how still is the working of Thy Will   That old
hymn verse I cant get it out of my mind and each
time I think of it again I shiver all over again
I shiver now   Well it is cold out here Raymond
Wingate black angel memorial wings or not
To the silent tomb just below us now they took my
Ed   Put him there in the ground yesterday
At least the earth was warm Journal it had been
sunny and the ground turned easy not like when
Alice was brought here that first time   It seemed
to me then I could not bear to have her taken out
that cold cold day in March put into the hard
ground to freeze   How I have learned to bear
unthinkable processions Journal I have havent I
All the people all the silly awkwardness all the

sheeplike words of calm submission to that Will
and then back to the house and the same great
groaning tables of food   How can they laugh and
talk just as if nothing had happened weather business sporting trips and so on   I look up over my
shoulder now at the wings of the black angel above
me   There is no laughter here and there should
be none no here at least there is dignity
Well Journal what a comfort you are   I am getting much attached to you Journal   Almost my
only comfort left   No there is still Taylor
I must not forget her   Right now she is still
standing here with the flowers holding her hat on
against the wind   How she has stayed by me
bless her   Journal a blessing how she has stayed
by me   But what else   Journal you see I am
getting desperate to find things to be thankful for
That is not so hard to understand is it ha

O yes   There is another thing to be thankful
about   The monument did come in time   I
thought it wouldnt but they put two teams of horses
on and got it here from the City the night before
the funeral   I had it done by that Julian Mabee
person and he did all right by me   It is now
green in the last light of the dusk but the carving
on it is clear   I ordered it a long time ago when
I first saw Ed was going to go fast   It is very
simple just a headstone on a small two step base
But the inscription I did myself   Wrote it I mean
not chisled it out on the stone Mabee did that but
I did write it myself   You didnt know that
Journal   A secret I have kept from you   Now
you wont be mad at me because I wrote in another

place besides in here will you   Please dont
I can see it now the lines of it if not each word on
Eds headstone   But I wrote them all I dont need
to see them they say this

> Unto Almighty God dear parents myself I adress
> I bid you goodbye in humble thankfulness
> Thanks for all your care on me bestowed
> The means of learning unto me allowed
> Leave me now I pray still to pursue
> A golden art the vulgar never knew

Not so bad if I do say so myself Journal   Dont
be mad now agree with me   This thing I have
for writing and the use of words   How glad I am
it has made me able to say something definite about
Ed   Something I know he would approve it saying he had his art the way it does
The wind blows harder now   Now I will go with
Taylor and put these flowers on the heads of my
children   Journal I hear voices   No I do I
hear voices calling me I do

Same day   Journal I am home   Yes it was real voices I
heard there was nothing wrong with me   I said
Taylor do you hear anything and she frowned and
pointed   She said yes there is some people coming to see you   My name sounded out again and
there was several figures coming through the dusk
and the tombstones calling for me   They were
shadowed on the body and the face because the
dusk was down and no more sunlight   I said who
is it   Then they came up closer   I saw David

and with him Charlie   I said what in the world
Are you worried about me I am all right   Then
Charlie said yes I know that I know that and
David said hush Charlie   David said I should
come on home now   I said all right as soon as
I place my flowers but then Journal I saw who was
with them   It was Susie Journal Susie and Arthur Moore the boy who courted my darling Evie
and also with them was O god William Craig
Whats this I said   Whats this why are these
awful people here with you   And I stood up and
hugged you Journal under my ladies walking cloak
whose flaps fell and the wind caught them and blew
them out back against the legs of the black marble
angel   Charlie then laughed a high and hard
laugh it hurt me when he did that but not so much
as a second later when he said look   Look at
them both up there in that wind   Hey Taylor he
shouted   You are closer than we are   Which
one is the black Angel of Death and which one is
her which is which   I broke down then and cried
out   I heard a sharp crack and seen that David
with his open hand in full swing had struck Charlie
and sent him to his knees   Then David come
slowly up to me but I would have none of David
then   Submit Journal submit to David then oh
no no no   I stood up and came down to them
calling upon Almighty God as my judge upon this
earth to strike them down for such a thing said to
me   For such treatment over the bodies of my
children so dearly beloved   Charlie would not
hear it   He jumped up from the ground even
his father could not stop him   He screamed at
me killer killer you killed them all   We know

now   We know all about you   Submit to that
Submit Journal   I thank God in his righteousness that he did not forsake me I felt his firm
hand tight as a vise on my shoulder and I walked
through them down from the black angel right
through them all as did Jesus through the crowd
with none to come with me except poor frightened
Taylor   I walked slowly home and I have put
myself to bed   I have drunk some tea and now
I am going to sleep   Journal thank you for your
patience in hearing me out   They are all in the
parlour now buzzing about like blow flies   I will
get my sorely needed sleep and then in the morning
I will get up and face them until they lower their
heads to me   Such miserable things as they are
I will sleep now and in the morning I will get up
and go on with it a woman dead with grief but
I will get up and go on and on no matter how
terible   Terible spelled terrible   Two rs

III

ANVIL

III

ANVIL

28　This afternoon through my bedroom window I heard
a clump out on the porch　　There was a piece of
paper wrapped around a rock somebody had thrown
there and run away　　Taylor brought it to me
It had written on it　　You have killed your children　　Shame on you　　Laugh or cry Journal
which

29　Could not go to Church yesterday and today I feel
bad missing Gods love and blessing　　Journal do

you love me   Do you   Did Fathers books love
him   All those nights he sat writing in them did
they care   No   Silent old book how can you
care about anything   You cant lucky thing you
I am going to study now one solid hour in both
the Dictionary and in Correct English Usage
Dr Rudge has put me to bed for one week at least
wont let them say anything more to me do anything
more until I am up

30 Today I have been studying hard Colbert Moreheads fine workbook in English   When I get good
enough I will start doing things right in here
It is very hot today   I had some belly cramps
Silly woman for a minute I thought I was young
again   O what a feeling   Nobody will tell me
anything about what they are doing   Hot again
I have sweat through the sheets twice   God only
knows what is happening to me but I think He has
forgotten me this time

May 1 Well there is nothing in no dictionary or in Moreheads Correct English to tell you Journal what is
happening now inside me   How I wish there was
some words and phrases that would do it   But
anyway you dont care any more than anyone else
do you   I hate you sometimes Journal but still I
put you in my bottom drawer with the sliding panel
where I alone know you lie and all day I think of
you   I will always treat you right and from now
on always write your name with a capital J Journal
just dont you forsake me

2 I am to get up tomorrow   Journal I must trust
you I have to I can see that now otherwise I cant

think   Dont be mad at me   But why should
you you are just an old book I have come to write
in a dumb illiterate woman   You are only paper
made from trees you dont care   But if you did
If by magic you did and you got mad at me now
like the rest O what would I do   I am scared
I dont think I want to write any more   Dr
Rudge coming again tonight

3 My own home   This home I brought into being
with these womans hands now it is my prison
How can they treat me like this even Taylor wont
say much they wont let her   David will only
barely smile   How can they   What are people
made of   You are trees and paper journal what
are we

4 I love you Journal your paper and ruled lines on
which I write and the feel of your back binding on
my thumb   Dont ever get mad at me   I hope
I dont dream tonight   I cant remember what I
dream but I do know they hurt   I asked David
yesterday when he came in bringing me a bowl of
apples and grapes and some flowers I said David
what are your dreams like   Theyre fun he said
dumping the flowers in a bowl they looked stringy
but they were flowers and are welcome   I said
what do you mean fun   He said well I sometimes
dream about catching big fish   He smiled and
said and sometimes I dream about flying through
the air like swimming through the water and about
fistfights that dont hurt that I win like a boy
I said David dont your dreams ever hurt   He
said oh sometimes there is a booger or something
after me but I know he cant catch me after all its

only a dream so I dont worry   I said David help
me   Then he frowned and said you just rest easy
Rest easy Journal can you believe it   Rest easy
like I was a horse thats what he said to me patted
my shoulder went out of the room   O to dream
about flying and winning fistfights and catching big
fish   A woman is different from a man   Journal what are you   Nothing   Neither   You
are not man or woman   Well bless you then

Same day They say I am getting stronger   I say what is
going on now   They say youll see when you get
stronger   But when will they let me get up

5 With the spring the town cats have started prowling
You can hear them late at night   They run under
the houses around here a lot   Dr Rudge says just
a few more days

6 Tonight a lot of people in the parlour   The doors
closed but I could hear a little   I heard Charlie
yelping out trial trial we got to have a trial
They say that in olden times the Indians would cut
a captives stomach open just a little and pull out
the intestine and nail it to a tree   Then they
would burn the captive so there was nothing to do
but run around the tree tearing himself and tying
himself up by his own intestines   O Journal how
my grandfather scared me when I was a little girl
listening to him tell such stories about the Indian
wars   Then when I was so scared he would just
beam and laugh and say thats all over   You dont
have to worry about savages now   Ha ha
Journal   Whoo hahaha

7 It is out now into the clear   It is done I can
see now what it is   Things are not so bad as I
thought I was just scared being kept alone and
ignorant thats all   Things are not so bad but
how my heart aches for Charlie   If only he could
see himself now the way he is   His eyes bulge
almost out of his head and his teeth stick out over
his lips and he chatters like a squirrel once he gets
to talking like that and cant stop himself   O
Charlie my poor boy   Well Journal this is what
its all about   At the Cemetary when they came
to me Charlie had brought them   He said to
David then that he had proved beyond any shadow
of doubt that I killed my children   Dont laugh
Journal thats what he said and the others didnt
know what to think   He brought William Craig
and Arthur Moore and Susie Balis to David and
David got confused with Charlies talk and let them
all come to me that way in the Cemetary

I see now what a paragraph is Journal   It is
to keep things seperate when they get complicated
the way they are now isnt it   I know that now
and will use them in the right way I hope   Didnt
need Colbert Moreheads book though to figure that
out

All right then   So we had that awful meeting
in the Cemetary   I went to bed   Dr Rudge
said I was not to be bothered until I had my
strength back and it rested there me going nearly
crazy in my bed alone waiting for strength
Finally last night was the time to meet again

Now David heard Charlie and the others out I
think until he had it all straight   Then about

the third night when I was sick he told Charlie no
that he was wrong and that it was finished
Charlie then said how about you Journal   Thats
right he put into Davids mind that I kept you for
awful reasons that in you was even more proof
So David asked me if I would let him read you and
I screamed no no you cant have my Journal too
and David didnt press me about it any more but
that made him confused again I guess   Then two
days ago when Taylor was helping me take a bath
we got back to the room and saw Charlie disappear
down the hall   He had been in my room trying
to get you Journal but you were safe in my panel
and he couldnt find you   Charlie tried to steal
you Journal all you mean to me now in this time
he tried to take away I want you to remember that
    So then Charlie my youngest son has accused me
his own mother of the killing of my children his
sister Evie his half brother Ed and his half sister
Alice   He has built up this great eventful case
against me poor Charlie and he has run about the
town telling everyone all about it my monstrous
doings   Even David couldnt stop him from doing
that though I think he has tried to   Which ex-
plains Journal why not one living soul came to visit
me in my sickness not even Mavis Grant   How
that hurt and still does even though I know the
reason for it now
    So Davids brow was wrinkled and he was sorely
puzzled when he came into my room to see me
Baggy pants foolish man he set on the bed and just
breathed there trying to smile and set up a situation
of calm and reason not knowing how to start speaking this craziness   I did it for him   I said

Well David it looks like I have killed all my children dont it are you going to hang me today or
tomorrow   He blushed and hung his head and
said Now dont say that   I said well what do you
expect me to say you are going around believing it
arent you   He said no of course not and he
looked out the window   I leaned back against
my pillows and waited   Then he said why dont
we just clear it all up quietly and have done with
it   We do have to convince Charlie you know
Even with what he is saying and the state he is in
he is still our son you know   I said well it is a
little hard for me to admit that right now but go
right ahead and clear it up quietly then   David
coughed and smiled and said fine you just let me
have your journal for ten minutes to show to Charlie   I promise it wont leave my hands he wont
touch it   Just let him see whats in it so hell
know for sure hes wrong

Just him David I said and he blinked then
What do you mean he said

I said just him that has to know hes wrong oh
David David you fool no a million times no   My
Journal is all I have left of me now that I can love
maybe you dont understand that but its true and
not Charlie not you nobody is going to see what I
have written and thats that

He stood up then   His foolish face becoming
firm and his puzzled look and wrinkled brow getting more puzzled and more wrinkled until it seemed
to me this is the way David will look forever

You wont let me read the journal then he said
No I said   No I will not
He rubbed his face with both hands and said

well all right then you are making me have to let
Charlie have his say

I said let him and so David did and presided over
it last night

I was brought into the parlour and seated ever
so comfortable in my chair   Taylor was on hand
with lots of tea   She was so scared I could see
her lips and adams apple tremble   Then when I
had one swallow of tea David started

He said Charlie has something to say   Then a
few others here have something to say   Then
we want to hear what you have to say and have
done with this matter   I said David thats all
right with me but I do wish you would all relax a
little and not fill the air with meanness and hatred
I am just a poor woman sitting here drinking tea
what do you think I am liable to do to you
I looked at William Craig who was there and he
got up and took his tea out on the porch a minute
I know to put something in it before coming back
in   Arthur Moore was there his hair all slicked
down looking just like the wonderful young eligible
bachelor he pretended to be when he courted my
darling Evie   And of course that Susie was there
too all pinch faced and sniffling about with her dark
eyes runny and upset behind them glasses   I said
well then carry on go ahead

David said Charlie you speak first but slowly

Charlie got up looked around very important and
serious coughed his throat clear and started in but
just as he did we heard a catfight   There has
been a wild Persian roaming around town now for
some time   Bristly fur all torn and matted a
mean creature   It was mixing with a bunch of

town cats outside you could hear the yowls of those town alleyrabbits and that wild Persian going at it They run right under the house and we could hear those awful humanlike wails and screeches That fierce cry upset Charlie he began to gulp and stammer   I said Charlie whats the matter you dont mind a little catfight do you   Everybody had to smile a little then even David   Journal I thought of you and how Charlie tried to steal you away from me   I thought of the love and devotion I gave each of my children every minute of my life   I thought of each painful groaning birth of my babies and also of how I came conscious with Charlie and saw his little head coming out of me for a second and of him now   Of this ridiculous thing being said to me and I felt then and there a tight grip a hand on my shoulder and a great strength and calmness and knew I had got my strength back all right   I offered my heart to my Saviour Jesus Christ   I gave myself up to his judgement alone and accepted his silent love and smiled at Charlie and said well go on son   What do you have to say to your mother

The wild Persian yowled under the house and Charlie just couldnt talk   David said well dammit wait a minute then   He got a broom from the kitchen and clomped around outside and poked under the house until in a fearful scream and screech they cleared out   All this time Charlie stared at me his mouth open   Poor David outside bending over hands and knees poking at the cats under the house and Charlie just standing mouth open like he had froze that way   I just sat and smiled   Charlie had to gulp finally gasp and

open up his fancy collar he was wearing a nicely
striped shirt one I had made for him   He had
to untie his little bow tie and it hung down loose
like a babies give out legs   His eyes bulged and
his front teeth lapped out there onto his bottom lip
He looked like something feebleminded thats what

David came back in   He said all right for the
cats lets get on with it   He said Charlie go slow
now you hear

Charlie started again but not slow   He has
always been a chatterbox Charlie but now it was
like his tongue was something partly caught in a
trap thrashing and wriggling   He went through
it faster and faster chattering and shaking and his
eyes bulging

Journal the rest tomorrow   I have got to get
some sleep now   I have future tasks I see that
now   I have a whole lot to do in the next few
days

8   Today I went to see William Craig   I will tell
you all about it dear Journal but first let me finish
about yesterday   My days are sure getting tangled up but I cant help that

Well Charlie stammered and stuttered it out that
I had indeed in fact killed my children   He said
first lets take Alice   I said thank god son you
cant take dear Alice anywhere she is out of your
insane grasp   He turned to William Craig sitting
on my mohair sofa and said what did Alice tell you
sir   Called William Craig sir right in my own
house that butcher with trembleing hands and rum
in his tea on my mohair sofa   William Craig
then said in his deep voice quavery his throat drip-

ping rum he said Alice told me she wanted the
operation done because her mother told her to
Charlie said Alice told you that   William Craig
said yes   Charlie said when did she say it
William Craig said when it was almost over when
it was too late for me to do anything for her
I said quick at what moment was that William
Craig was it when you had your filthy hands
plunged into her sweet flesh tearing it apart
David said Now now and I distained to say any
more   Charlie said so then Alice told you she
didnt want the operation at all but her mother made
her go to you and get it   William Craig blinked
at that   Drunkard and murderer he is but not
a liar I guess He said no what Alice said was
Mamma told me to thats all   Charlie started in
again trying to put words in the mans mouth but
David took a stand said Charlie thats enough go
on to the next one   Charlie swallowed said all
right wiped his brow said to me theres more dont
worry   I said O Charlie what is it you want
from me   He said nothing I want you in prison
convicted of murder thats all   Wiping his face
saying dont worry I know Im next on your list this
is my last chance dont you think Ill make the most
of it   I just sighed resigned myself said go on
then   Charlie called upon Arthur Moore who sat
up in his chair and smiled like the innocent handsome young man he pretends to be

Charlie said what did Evie tell you about her
headaches   Arthur Moore said Evie told me she
had always had them except when she went off to
school and got out of the house   And she said
that now she had to keep coming back so much that

the headaches were getting worse and she didnt think she could stand it   I said what do you know about my darling Evies headaches Arthur Moore it wasnt her precious head you was interested in   David said now now I sighed resigned myself said go on then

Charlie said what else   Arthur Moore said what do you mean what else   Charlie said tell them man how Evie told you her mother was causing her head to split open keeping her in the house all the time driving her to her death tell them   Arthur Moore a foolish immoral young wag but he was not a liar either and he said Charlie wait a minute now I never said that   What Evie told me was that her headaches were worse when she was home now thats all Charlie   Then Charlies eyes bulged and his teeth chattered and he yelped damn you Arthur Moore you tell them all you told me

Arthur Moore then said Charlie whatever else you think I might have said is your imagination

Charlie raved then and David took him firmly by the arm and said quietly go on son to the next one and Charlie said Susie Susie tell them tell them oh Susie tell them what Ed told you

Susie Balis who loved my dying boy a silly and wishywashy girl but not a liar neither   She said Charlie I thought all these other people had worse things to say than they do   All Ed told me was this   Many times he told me that he was dying of love

Yes screamed Charlie whose love

Susie said he never told me whose love Charlie he always said just love thats all   And I know

it wasnt love of me said Susie Balis her eyes runny
with tears behind the glasses a foolish girl but a
truthful one Journal

Charlie screeched then like the wild Persian
Dying of love yes he said but whose love hers hers
hers   He pointed his poor shaking hand at me
like he was some capable lawyer poor Charlie
Her love he said yes she has loved us all thats right
she has loved us all to death

I said Charlie you arent dead son   I am doing
you no harm

Charlie was speechless then choking on his feelings and seemed about to fly all apart with his rage
at me my poor helpless Charlie   He glared at me
and turned to the others saying well what about this
now what about it what Ed said dying of love how
about that now

I stood up   I said I think I know what love
Ed meant   I was his mother and I knew my own
boy   If you will just come with me please
I went to my room got the key to Eds room upstairs
They all got up and followed even William Craig
I climbed the steps slowly with a wonderful dignity
not mine but given to me then in time of need
by Jesus in his love and righteousness   I un-
locked the door of Eds room and went in fixed
the lamp held it up and pulled the bedsheet down
from in front of the big canvas   There spread
across the wall the great awful painting of the
shapes and nameless things the animals the frog
dead the crokadile with the hideous naked member
the sword tied to it the kangaroo chewing her nipples the hedgehog in the pouch it all jumped out
at them in the light   They all gasped   I said

well that was what my poor Ed loved   That was it Ed was dying of love for this his diseased art and painting   It was love of this sickness you yourselves see in front of you

Susie cried   I think it is wonderful she said God bless him and she put her face in her hands and just run out of the room and away   William Craig downded the last of his rum tea and left Young Arthur Moore just stared with that blank childish face the stare of a man who has given himself to pleasure faced with something else then he swallowed once and left   That left just me David and Charlie in the room

David who had not seen the painting because he had forbeared to go where I did not want him said to me Poor Ed   I am sorry you knew about this and did not let me help you carry the burden that is what I am for you know   I said David you have carried many burdens for me I have carried this one alone he was not your son after all though I know how you loved him he was mine   David said all right then and he looked at Charlie and said it just wont hold up son and walked out of the room

That left me and Charlie there in the room alone Charlie had not seen the big diseased painting either only the drawings   He was staring at it and did not notice David was gone and just me there in the room alone with him

I said Charlie

Charlie turned and jumped then seeing there was nobody in the room but me   My poor Charlie such a jittery good for nothing except the wearing of fancy jackets and boaters   I said son look at it go ahead look at it   That was Eds diseased mind

Look just look you can see it up there in front of you on the wall

Charlie gaped looked around quick but they had all left him   His wild accusations had come to nothing   He gaped at me this last child of mine who treated me so awful accusing me of the worst act of mortal life and had meant it had meant and still did mean to do me in his own mother

I said look at the wall Charlie   That is your brothers mind up there   There is no wonder you might imagine such awful things about me   You have the same mind Charlie   I am sorry for you son   God help you and bless you

Then I left him there in the room with the diseased painting and went down to see Taylor who was hiding in the kitchen too scared to move   I said dont worry Taylor I am all right they didnt hurt me   Soon we heard Charlie run out of the house

I will tell you about William Craig some other time   As for Charlie he has been running all around the town again telling people I am a murderer and must be convicted before I get him too
O what a shame and pity poor boy   I told my sweet little Taylor about it all that dear thing
She brightly said to me never you mind that you dont have anything to worry about now

9 Tonight I have been to Temperence meeting
Down the street Journal my back straight my pace a measured and tranquil one   Not a word spoken to me by a soul hardly   Mavis Grant did not just cross the street to avoid me she went inside the first house she saw that had a lighted window

149

Over my shoulder I saw her come out again only
when I had passed   Mrs Fanny Knap did do me
the honor the grand honor of one short bob of the
head just that one nod and then scoot   Rev Bayley came up to me with a broad smile saying oh how
are you let me take your hand and I thought O yes
the men of God when the chips are thrown down
there on the floor it is to them we must finally turn
But Journal he was in such a hurry said good-
evening so fast I could hardly make it out then ex-
cuse me away he went looking about to see if any
had caught him paying that little courtesy to me
I blushed and my face stung like it had been
slapped   But then I took thought   They are
simply frightened   They hang back because they
do not know what trouble might come to them what
possible taint   So they run and they hide
Will never come forth to discover anything until it
is published all over the world for them   Poor
cowardly people but it is them who has fear not me
after all   I felt my strength again   My Redeemer held fast to my shoulder that tight grip I
was strong and measured in my pace   I went in
to the Temperence meeting and sat alone   No
one said anything to me at all except Mrs Nutt
She was there all right with her rich fancy dress
that doesnt do that frame one bit of good her grand
airs that dont help her any the bony thing that she
is   She is temporary Superintendant now until
the organization is complete and final elections held
well you know what that means no one is going to
run any thing here except Mrs. Nutt   Well she
said something to me all right   She stopped
where I sat and with her sweetest deadly smile said

and how are you these days my dear and passed on in triumph   I took part alone

I have to remember about these paragraphs

They still havent decided on a name cant get hold of one bold enough   Nobody could think of anything except Temperence Union and thats so tame Then Mrs Nutt said well how about a slogan then and something popped into my head   I thought of a kingdom overthrown Journal   It made shivers go up and down my back   Yes a kingdom overthrown with its mighty monarch struck down from the high royal perch and throne   I stood right up said how about this and I said

Tremble world at hand is a great fall
Down forever with King Alcohol

There was a big stir of approval Journal but Mrs Nutt stared it down with a tipping of that long nose and a wrinkling of those big nostrils   She huffed and said it would be considered   Nobody else could think up one so on we went then to the testimonials and there were lots of those   Many people got up to bravely testify the ruin caused by King Alcohol not flinching about being specific in the naming of actual cases they had knowledge of Every now and then someone would steal a glance at me   I know they liked my slogan   I just love it Journal dont you   Gives me goose pimples I dont know just why but it does

12 Sunday   Went to Church   I received no Christian word however from any person   What wounds they inflict with tight smiles and a shifting

of place in the pews   But I held fast and was all right until I felt somebody sit down next to me during the opening hymn   I smiled and turned to bless silently whoever was doing this kindness to me a poor woman outcast from human society for no reason   I didnt smile long   It was William Craig   He was smiling too but when he seen it was me he didnt smile long either started to move again but it was too late then   So he stayed there plump next to me and then he turned and grinned at me   No wheres the Dictionary   Yes thats the word   Leered   He leered at me   I had to sit and endure his breath all through the service and thought it would never come to an end Walked home alone   David not feeling well at all   He says nothing but I know he thinks about Charlie   People only see Charlie at night now in the saloon

13   Worked hard today   My aches help me   Took up all the upstairs carpets   Taylor such a help So young and strong   That slim body bending and pulling and fixing for me so easily   God bless the young and able

Same day   Prophecy Journal in what you just write down day to day   I had finished my entry for today and had gone to bed   Thought David was still at the store   Then I was awoke by a sound of great sobbing   I hopped out of bed and standing in the parlour David my husband the calmest and steadiest of all living men   He was weeping and began blundering about hand over his face I thought he was drunk   I said David David   He said oh oh

god dam it all and threw himself into a chair   It
was the old straightback rocker and it broke   Flew
apart and David fell sat bump on the floor   He
swore again and took the pieces of the chair and
threw them against the wall   It was so scary
seeing him in such a state I said David David what
is it and he told me with the first tears I have ever
seen come from him

Somebody came to the store said you best go see
to your son   Prophecy Journal didnt I write only
yesterday Charlie was nowhere to be found now
but in the saloon   Well there he was by this time
people tired listening to him in drunken rage carrying on about me his own mother trying to kill him
So when David got there Charlie with his smart
clothes once so gay now all smeared and dirtied
and nasty he was on the sawdust floor of that
unspeakable place   He was drunk and sick and
he was in a fit banging his head against the brass
footrail   David got hold of him but Charlie
then let out a terrible scream then grabbed David
and cried and cried   David and some men took
him back to the store   Got him calmed down
until David made the suggestion Charlie should
come home and go to bed   That threw Charlie
into his spasm again   So David knew then there
was nothing to do   He gave Charlie some money
and Charlie has gone back to the City   Dear God
says David how long do you think he will last there
the way he is now and then David wept it all out
and I let him be   O Charlie my poor last child
my bright little boy King Alcohol got you and you
lost your hold didnt you

Charlie you were such a bright boy   Shiny

and so full of fun   I remember once when you
came into my kitchen in the afternoon   You were
only nine or ten years old that day and you had
a little black mask over your eyes   You thought
no one could tell it was you because you had on
that mask   You had a pistol made from two
sticks and you said stick up your hands Lady I am
going to rob this place   I said O help and pretended such fright   I threw my hands high in
the air saying do spare my life and I let you make
off with a blackberry tart   Then that night at
supper I said Charlie Im sorry but you cant have
dessert like the others because yours was stolen
this afternoon   Yes a bold racoon came in the
kitchen while I was cooking and stole it away
You was so surprized   You said a what stole it
and I said a little racoon because it had its little
black mask on   You took some better stock of
your mother then

I wish you had taken better stock of me these
last days Charlie   Then maybe you wouldnt be
running from me crazy in your head on the roads
at night toward the great awful lonly City right now
but it serves you right son

O Charlie bold racoon

14 Charlies flight and disgrace has got around quick
    O this town   Mavis Grant came to the door
    Brought me some pudding   I took it thanked her
    and closed the door

15 Today in the pantry I had a sinking spell   Put
    my hand over my eyes felt the same old dizziness
    My heart yearned again for my beloved children

I felt sorry and sick for Charlie even   Taylor
came up put her strong hands on my shoulder
Hold on she said just hold on   She sat me down
in the kitchen got me some water   I said Taylor
why are you so good to me why have you been so
steadfast I never gave you that raise you wanted
She tried to think about it took me very seriously and went down on a knee in front of the chair
thinking   She isnt very intelligent Taylor isnt
but she tried to think it out   Her eyes strained
and she stared at the leg of the chair and her face
was a little twisted   Finally she said I have
learned about human misery from you   I said oh
well Taylor I guess you have and Im sorry for that
She said no oh no you have changed me from a silly
girl into a woman   I did that Taylor I said
She said yes with your suffering and the way you
have held up under it   I felt so good then   I
said oh it is not me but the firm hand on my shoulder you fine girl   A pot of carrots on the stove
boiled over then and she got up to see to that
What would I do without her that little girl so full
of sympathy and understanding   Her soul Journal is white as snow this I here inscribe dear Taylor
even if your beautiful body is black

16 David sick   Has been in bed all day   I fed
him soup but he couldnt hold it down

17 David better still quesy in the stomach and still
in bed   I took good hold of my house again today   Taylor and I made the dirt fly let me tell
you that Journal   We even sang a song or two

18   David up back to the store   No news from Charlie in the City   Have written to his old boss and David wrote to the boarding house to see if they have seen him   What do you think will happen to him now Journal I just dont know do you

19   Did not go to Church today   Let them wonder just how much they have wronged me

20   Scrubbed the kitchen floors cleaned out the stove painted part of the pantry   Good day

Same day   I am in bed now   Cant sleep   Something has been nagging at me Journal   What is it   I dont know do you

Same day   I have read back over you Journal and I see now I never told you about my visit to William Craig the day after the awful scene in the house here with Charlie   Forgot all about that somehow Maybe thats whats been bothering me   Lets see O well I am too sleepy now   Tomorrow Journal

21   Good day today   Cleaned all winter ashes out of the fireplace hadnt been done because of all the confusion here   Scrubbed the bricks and washed it all down   Good day   Yes I feel fine today

Same day   Forgot about William Craig again   Still it isnt just that nagging at me is it   Well maybe I best get him out of the way and try to clear up whats bothering me   All so mixed up now happening so fast   And remember your paragraphs old girl The day after the scene with Charlie I went to

see William Craig   It was noon   I found his
house the other end of town   Taylor went with
me waited in the street   He has rented his house
out now all but one side of the front   There he
lives now alone   I knocked and he came to the
door in a dressing gown at high noon   Half drunk
of course

I said   Can I come in

He said   No

I said   Well dont you think you owe me a visit
after all you just paid me one

He said   All right come in

I went in   The place was a terrible shambles
Filthy   I sat down in a chair with stains and
smells all over it   Sat as lightly as I could
He said   Well what do you want

I said   I want you to tell me about Alice all
about it beginning to end   Everything that happened

He laughed   I have served my term in prison
do you think I am going to let you send me there
again he said

I said   No thats not it and then there was a cry
of children Journal   He has rented the house out
to a farmer moved into town with five small children   They were whining and wailing away
about something in the clear and pleasant beseech-
ing way a child has bless them all dear things

I said   How can you stand this   Living here
where you hear children cry all the time after what
you have done

That got him   He said dam you and he went
to a bottle on the mantlepiece and drank from it
Stood there shaking and figiting me as calm as

Keith River at summer noon

I said   You tell me about Alice beginning to end
and I will not ever bother you again   I will leave
you alone forever sir

My god he said is that a promise woman

I said   Yes it was

He said All right   He said Your girl Alice
came here that night   I was out seeing pa-
tients   I drove up in my trap and she was on the
porch   She run up to me before I could even get
out of my trap saying you have got to do it you
have got to   I said do what   She said help me
I said   All right first calm down and I brought
her inside a big mistake   She told me what she
wanted   I said what month are you in   She
said second month   I said well this is possible
but I dont like it why do you have to have it done
Then she pulled the pistol out of her purse
Didnt say anything just pulled it out and put the
barrel into her mouth   Then speaking as best
she could with a gun in her mouth she said   Are
you going to do it or not   Now I am not a hero
after all   She wanted an abortion had a gun to
use on herself and or me too   I said good god
girl all right all right it will cost you one hundred
dollars   She threw her purse at me   There was
eighty eight dollars there   Take that its all I can
get she said   I said all right now give me the
gun   She said no the gun stays right here in my
hand all the time   Thats impossible and dangerous I said   Oh no she said get me some strong
cord   I did   She wrapped the cord around the
pistol and her hand tying it tight through the trigger
guard and around the butt and barrel so it wouldnt

158

fall away from her hand   I gave her some whiskey to drink gave it to her watching that gun tied to her hand as scared as I have ever been   She got drunk a little said thats enough and I laid her out on my table but every time I reached for the gun and the cord where it was tied in knots around her hand the pistol barrel bobbed at me and she was ready to shoot one of us which I could never tell   You sure you want me to go on with this William Craig said

I said   Yes I am sure

He said   Well I was so nervous about that dam pistol I hit her too hard in there   It started quick too quick   She had convulsions and knew it was going too fast I think anyway the gun came up and I grabbed her hand my god even in the throes of that rupture she fought me and because of the cord I couldnt get it loose   Which of us she would have killed I dont know both maybe
Anyway by the time I got the chord untied and the pistol out of her hand and turned to throw it away it was too late for both of us   Too late for her because it had come too fast and hard out of her and too late for me because there were people looking in my window and coming in the door and I was finished too   Because of the gun I hadnt been able to muffle her screams you see I had forgot about that nervous as I was

I said   What did she scream   Did she scream just what you told us yesterday at my house

He said   Yes just that   While I was holding her hand she kept yelling Mother told me to Mother told me to   And woman it was a good thing those people at the window and door saw her with the

gun and me trying to get it away from her else I
would be in prison yet you know

That awful man   I looked around at his filthy
rooms   The children of the farmer come to town
and renting his house was crying but some of them
laughing too   I looked out the window where a
piece of rope had been hung knotted from an elm
for them to fool with   A little girl with long
curly locks of hair was hitting at it and humming
to herself

I said   William Craig do you think you are not
in prison now   Look around you you sot
How can you live my man this way

Get out of here he said you devil

I said   All right a bargain is a bargain   I will
never bother you again   Just let me be sure
Did she say anything else about me

He said   No

I got up and was halfway out the door

He said   Oh wait a minute there was one other
thing not about you but there was one other thing

I didnt turn just said what

He said   When she was a little drunk she kept
whispering something about Christs cave the cave
of Jesus   I didnt know what that meant
Thats all

What Christs cave I said

I dont know he said and thats all

I said   Goodbye then and went on out   You
see Charlie how wrong you were   Poor boy
I never in my life told Alice to have that abortion
done to do such a thing that ended so horribly
Never

I stopped in the yard and the little girl with the
curly locks was holding onto the piece of rope where

her father must have knotted it for her   She was
stepping back and then swinging on it her curls
flowing out behind her then slapping the back of
her little neck on the backswing

I said   Hello honey you having fun

Wheee   she said swinging

I came on home   Satisfied about Alice finally
and that William Craig was doomed to a quick
liquid death I didnt need to prosecute him any more
and very satisfied that Alice brought her death
upon herself by getting near that man bless her
Alice I forgive you with all my heart

I wonder though what she meant by Christs cave
You ever hear of that Journal   Also why I got
mixed up in my dates and didnt put this down until
now

O well too tired I guess   So much has occured
so fast   Goodnight Journal

22 Arthur Moore works in the bank   I had some
kitchen money I needed to put into the account
I took it there and said   Here Arthur will you de-
posit this for me

He said   Yes mam

I said   Arthur can you talk to me sometime
about Evie   I would appreciate it

He said   All right   I can now if you want

I said   Good

He saw Mr Coley of the bank who said sure go
ahead just be back soon and we took a walk down
the street

I said   Arthur   What did Evie tell you about
her headaches when you were courting her tell me
all you know

I already have he said   Evie felt her headaches were worse when she was at home just like I said

I said   Arthur did she want to leave home and marry you really

She couldnt make up her mind he said

I said   Why not

She said she loved you too much to go away and leave you   She told me she was all you had to lean upon all you had left and to leave you would be to kill you

I said   Oh

She kept telling me that before marriage she had to learn to be smart in school learn to read all the books and make something more of herself   She said she just didnt have the full education to marry me yet   You know she was a fine girl God bless her but she wasnt so bright not really

O yes I said   O yes she was too Arthur

No he said   She just felt she had to be   She would try to read a book the way a man would try to cut through a tree trunk with a pocket knife
She would have been fine as Mrs Arthur Moore though   I never could figure what it was she was so desperate to learn reading those books until her head was about to bust

I said   Well she was a good and industrious student Arthur

Maybe he said   Anyway she loved you industriously thats a fact

I held his arm tight   O Arthur Moore I said Thank you so much for telling me this   I did not know just how much my sweet Evie cared for her mother   Thank you

Then I took my hand away and left him

But wait a minute here   he said

I said   Thank you son you have told me what I wanted to know and I left him

You see Charlie   O how sweet it is to know my darling Evie loved her mother   Not like you Charlie and I wonder where you are right this minute Journal   Whats going on with him now do you suppose   O darling Evie

23   Couldnt work today   Every time I tried to get something done Id just make a mess   Getting these fits of being so tired   They come on me right after breakfast   Whats wrong   Wheres the tight hand on my shoulder I dont feel it like I did

24   Journal I am so confused   Help me please

26   Sick all day   Went to bed with bowl of apples you pen and ink Journal but I didnt have anything to write   Got up and dressed   Made David get up and dress   He said for gods sake what do you want to do this for   I said never you mind come on   The school house was all dark   No moon to light the way   Had trouble with the steps there up to the door almost stumbled once It was after midnight and nobody answered David when he knocked and knocked   Got to Mr Rawlings house finally the headmaster and after I made David knock and knock he came to the door in a long nightshirt   What a flopped out pot belly he has not like when he is dressed tight and handsome in his dark suits at all   We asked for Susie and he said Yes Susie Balis she boards here now thats

163

right   I said where   He said well the girls are
all asleep now and looked at me funny   You
cant see her now he said

I said David

David took him aside talked a minute said I
know not what but convinced him found out what
part of what building and we left Mr Rawlings in
his night shirt and went there with a key

She was asleep in a room with two other girls
Each in thin beds up against the wall   I shook
the wrong girl and woke her up came near scaring
her to death then Susie popped up from bed   I
said Susie I must talk to you and she said all right
and we waited for her outside the room   When
she came out dressed in a gown I grabbed her wrist
and said listen here Susie

Ow said Susie let me go and she jumped back
David said we are going to wake everybody up and
cause a ruckus is that what you want   I said no
come on lets go outside on the lawn   Susie I said
come on with us now

She stood sniffling a little scared too such a weak
girl   Let me get my glasses then she said

You dont need glasses to speak the truth I said
just come on with us outside where we can talk
Then David talked to her softly and said it was all
right and so she came then   Walking with David
behind me

Outside on the lawn it was dark and poor
wretched girl she couldnt hardly see where she was
going and almost fell over some tree roots   I
grabbed her and held her up   She was confused
and dizzy   I told David go on over there now
and let me talk to her   David said wait a minute and I yelled at him and he went

Susie stood there in the dark her eyes all runny almost crying she was   Trying to see me clear but I stepped back a ways into the darkness and said   Now Susie you will tell me now I mean to know everything he said to you

I got just a bit of jabbering and whimpering out of her she was so scared and so flimsy that poor girl   The idea that she could ever have been a fit wife for Ed   She still couldnt see just where I was in the darkness and I kept back and asked her about her and Ed

Yes she said yes thats true Ed wanted to marry me thats true you know that   Did you have to get me up in the middle of the night to find that out   Where are you I cant see you she kept saying

Im right here I said   Control yourself and show a little backbone and answer me   She hushed up then and stood sniffling in the dark   I reached out and grabbed her wrist and she jumped back and stood shivering   Talk I said

Yes he wanted to marry me she said   And I only wish he could have found the way to do it before he died   Maybe I could have given him something before he died something

I laughed then   I said I suspect you were ready to do that all along Susie   What I want to know is what all he said to you   Never mind what you were so ready to give him I dont think Im interested in that

No I dont guess you are said Susie   Then she took a deep breath and said all right then Ed asked me to marry him and I said oh yes Ed Ill be yours and you have made me so happy   And I threw my arms around him and held him tight and

thought of all the things I wanted to do for him
because I loved him so much   And we were so
happy then

Susie sniffled and sniffled as she told it how
shameless she was in her spineless trembling

But then said Susie when I saw him the next day
he asked me again would I marry him   I said
yes of course David darling and he smiled but then
later he asked me again and kept doing that over
and over as if it hadnt been decided the first time
Finally I told him Ed why dont you just take
me away from here lets go now and then he said
it looking right at me smiling but saying oh Evie
you know you couldnt ever leave Mama   I said
Ed Im Susie Ed not Evie and he took me in his arms
and said why Susie hush I was only kidding you I
didnt mean that and wouldnt talk anymore   Still
I could have saved him   Even so I could have
saved him   I loved him   Is this what you
came to hear

Journal that jabbering wretched crying girl to
tell me such a thing that pitiful creature that lying
girl   No it is not I said   I did not come here
for you to tell me lies and fancies   I came for
the truth about my son in his last days of life before I got rid of you so he could die in peace
What kind of awful things are you trying to say
to me   No I didnt come to hear this

What did you come for then said Susie   To
hear me tell you he loved you more than me

I moved back in the darkness where she couldnt
see me and said yes

Oh well then he did   Of course he did   But
he loved Evie more than either of us and how you
brought that about god only knows

What do you mean I yelled at her that filthy awful girl

You know what I mean she said and she moved crying toward where she thought I was   Where are you she said   She moved past me and I came up beside her

Here I am you little fool I said

She jumped and turned and raised her hand as if to hit me Journal   I stood there staring at her and she wailed then and sank down in a fit on the ground   I felt so disgusted at her   I knew I should not have expected her to talk calmly without crying so spineless she is that girl no backbone at all   I stood there calm and strong while she cried and David came up thinking what kind of a woman she would have been for my Ed how pitiful and weak a creature

She sat there crying that she loved him Enough to turn a stomach   David came up and helped her stand   I said no I cant get nothing more out of her take her back and David did her sniffling and crying all the way until they went in the building

I stood in the dark then thankful I got rid of her so Ed could die in peace   To think of such things about Evie and Ed   What a terrible way for her to treat me to say such things after all my kindness to her

Same day   Cant sleep not even now   Early in the morning Lots of mist on the grass outside   David put me to bed but just cant sleep there is nothing else to write though is there Journal   Journal what else   Journal help me please   When I look out of my window into the backyard I see

the place where the grass stops by the chicken-
house and in the mist there I almost see Ed and
Evie playing the way they always did   How I
loved them playing together and how devoted they
were to me and to our home god bless them now
What is it I have yet to write   What is it Journal I have to say to you   Something something
but what   O Lord Im not going to be able to
sleep any at all   Why is that

27 All day my shoulder has ached for the firm hand to
grip it and steady me   No hand at all no touch
I started to go out of the house feeling I would
not mind what anybody said or did not say   But
down the street I saw ugly Mrs Nutt coming
She came closer walking past my house and I got
nervous and almost had the shakes for no real reason at all   So ugly and bony that woman so cold
and mean what must she be like to Calistra what
must she be like to her people   I stopped thinking about that pulled myself up went forward to
walk down my steps and onto the street and keep
on and pass but I couldnt   I got dizzy ran back
into the house I couldnt face her that awful woman
      But why

28 Today I tried to talk to David some   He said
its just nerves   Just nerves Journal   Taylor
killed a rat in the back yard with the hoe and for
some reason I thought I would die   I have been
in bed all afternoon

29 Years ago Journal so long ago Christs cave thats
where my mother told me I would be put if I ever

got into trouble with a man   The cave of Jesus
is where I would be banished have to give birth
there alone in the dirt

30   Journal I must go slow now one day at a time
Journal did I ever tell Alice about Christs cave
I cant remember everything I told my darling can
I   Only you might have been able to tell me
if I did   I didnt start you soon enough dam you

31   Maybe I did   I must have   I must have told
Alice   But when

June 1   Couldnt get out of bed all day   O my darlings
My heart is bursting   Outside God plays with
me flaunting fine weather in my face   The wind
and the flowers blow and nod   Christ Jesus wont
you put your hand on my shoulder again   O just
one touch   I am bursting

2   What did I tell them   Alice Evie Ed in all those
years   Who can remember all of it   It is hope-
less   Journal help me   I will trust in you you
are all I have now

3   That little girl swinging on that rope   Wheeeee
she said   She was laughing and swinging free as
a bird   I cant move in this bed hardly

4   O dear God

5   Journal Journal Journal help me   I am falling
into the black pits every one there is   I am burning   Catch me save me   I am on fire like the

169

great City   I am being consumed and thrown
down into the blackness   Jesus will not touch
my shoulder now   O Journal you are all I have
Help me help

6   Nothing

7   Wanted to go to town   See peoples faces   Get
out of the house   I only got to the edge of the
stores   A new young man has taken Charlie
Robinsons blacksmith shop   He was working
hard   Had taken the metal out of the forge
Had his bellows around his neck on a thong
Had the metal in the pinchers laid down on the
anvil   Was pounding it with the great hammer
thats sharp one end blunt the other   The metal
on the anvil was pounded and pounded and pounded
and the sound of it rang and rang   I cried out
and ran back down the street and into the house
Taylor is going to make me some tea

8   Christ I always thought you loved us   How
could you say we are gilty of what we dont even
remember   How can you say such a thing to me
If he does Journal then hes wrong Jesus is wrong
Isnt that right isnt it   How could I kill them

9   Journal this is what the Dictionary has to say
     Murder   1   killing a human being
           2   to mutilate or spoil or to de-
form by wretched performance   to mangle
to butcher   to commit murder

O thats plain

10   David just came to tell me the news about Charlie
He had a letter from James Hartwell in the City
Told me all about it without much emotion   How
does David do it I always will wonder though that
is not important now

James Hartwell wrote him that Charlie got hurt
in a saloon fight in the City   He wrote that
Charlie was drinking a lot and got mad at some
woman there and cursed her and then hit her and
that started a different fight or something and some
people hurt Charlie and the police came and he is
in jail now   Mr Hartwell said Charlie told the
jailer there he would not see nobody at all no
friends or relations at all and in no wise his own
parents and that as soon as they let him go he
would be gone for good and so there was no need
for anybody to come to see him

James Hartwell said he couldnt see Charlie because of that but that the jailers said he was acting pretty wild   He said something ought to be
done for him

David said   Well come on lets get ready and
maybe we can get on the afternoon train but I said
no

What do you mean no said David

Am I then to travel through the countryside
breathless to go to the side of a boy who wont see
me a boy who has accused me of the awful things
he did   Am I to do that David the answer is no
I said

For Gods sake said David cant you forget that
now   What is wrong with you

Nothing I said   And no I cant forget it so you

better go on by yourself if you want to get on that train

David glared at me and shook his head and started to say something then looked at the clock gulped and ran to put a few things together   In a minute it seemed a long time me standing there waiting not going to lift a hand to help him get ready but in a minute he went out the door and was gone

O Journal it wasnt true what I said to David Would I not go anywhere if Charlie was there hurt but Journal what if I went there and Charlie was dead too   I felt if I went he would be and I would have to gaze upon his lifeless face   What would I say to that gaze what

No more for me   No more funerals no more black angels   I want to be in this house alone now

11   Nothing

12   Nothing

13   Have not heard anything about David or Charlie yet   Must turn my mind elsewhere   Have been studying my Dictionary and Use of English Has been so hot   Outside now there is going to be an electrical storm everything very greenish I have slept and dreamed on and off more asleep dreaming than awake these last two days Couldnt write at all the pen it seemed too heavy to take up   Now I can write though say hello Journal and that is something at least   What would I do without you and Taylor and Jesus Christ my Saviour but I wonder what he thinks of

me now rising away up into his beautiful purple
and golden heaven

14 O Journal when I married Edward all those years
ago my first husband both of us young and eager
so sure and untiring   Well his unsuspected rage
so quickly let loose against me oh what that did
His anger because I did not every minute of my
womans life think only of him drove me then to my
children Alice and little Ed the only ones who would
always care for me no matter what I said or did
paragraph

    They tolerated me   They cared for me   My
poor ways were fine with them   Then Edward
died a heart attack I think of that same rage and
anger I uncorked in the man somehow like a selzer
bottle   I could not Journal face it alone could I
No not with two needy children me a widow in
this world without even a mite   The children
were growing up growing into knowledge of me seeing there was sometime reason to defy mother
So I married David when he blurted out a proposal
to me that day at a turkey shoot when he had won
the thing   Even with my poor eyes I could see
Davids nature was not Edwards and wouldnt ever
be and David had the store then   No more Edward for me no more anger black wrath and boiling
impatience   I could not stand that any more
So you see I took David who has been just what I
thought who has never raised his voice to me hardly
much less his hand David kind and tolerant and
good himself so at peace with the world hes been
worse than Edward and my pain the same paragraph

    So it is true then that Edwards rage was mine as

well for I seized upon it and made it my own did
I not   It is true that Davids weakness and simple minded wishywashy life is mine for I took it
to me something to scorn and feed upon   All of
it then was mine

Then what was Edward all those years ago
What our children Alice and Ed   What is David
now and what the two from him my dear Evie with
her hurting brow and poor bold Charlie   Edward
David my husbands all those years what were you
where were you all that time   Why didnt you
keep me from burying myself all I am into the frail
lives of my children

Dam husbands

O God   I am so confused about it all   I
dont know

I am a broken thing   A shell   Throw me
away

15   This afternoon I took a nap   Had to lay down
Taylor working in the kitchen'   Wind blowing
you could hear it could feel the rain coming on
Still greenish outside two days in a row but until
then no sign of storm just wind   I woke up
in the afternoon and was so confused   I had
dreamed such a beautiful thing   My brother
Henry was dead and had come for me   He took
me down the steps out of the house and where the
street used to be was a great silver river of pure
shining water   He took me by the hand and I
followed him into it   I was scared I would choke
as the waters closed over my face but Henry smiled
and I was then breathing water and feeling so fine
We floated along talking about the old times we

had so long ago   Then we rose up out of the
water and my clothes had changed from my old
dress into snow white rainment and I stood in front
of a house   This house   My own home except
it too now was as silver shining like a great star
And from the front door opening came them all
Clean and shining happy in white rainment
They came and kissed me and said O mother welcome   God knows how we have missed you and
waited for you   Come inside and have some tea
    Then the wind woke me up thunder and the rain
beginning   Alone and dreary in this house I need
you Journal   I need to put down what I had
dreamed so beautiful it was so awful to wake up
and lose it   I was wandering around changing
clothes because I had sweated through my gown
Thinking about what to write how to get the memory of it   You can describe a dream I found but
you never touch it really that way   The rich thing
itself is lost in just a minute of wandering and
thinking   You have so many different things so
rich and fresh in mind and memory that turning
from one to the other you lose them all   And
write what I just did   God knows that doesnt
say what it was like in that pure silver water or
standing before the shining house with all of them
coming down the porch their arms out
    There was somebody knocking then on the door
I heard it called Taylor but it was afternoon then
Taylor was gone to the stores   I went downstairs
carrying you Journal dear in my arms but confused
because of the dream and the changing of clothes
so forgetting I had no clothes on at all   I was
naked as the day of my birth thats the fact   I

just missed that somehow forgot about it and I flung open the door

There was a great gust of wind and the crackle of electrical storm   The wind hit my nakedness and shocked me and pouring in through the door the air was wet and hard pushed by the storm that was bending the treetops on the street and billowing way out the skirts and frills and ruffles of Mavis Grant Fanny Knap and Mrs Nutt   All standing there with fruit and some cloth covered supper on a tray and a bowl of oranges   They gasped

My Lord says Mrs Nutt

O dont my Lord me Mrs Nutt I said   I laughed at her then waving you about Journal with my hair falling down over my eyes   What do you women want here I said

They stood there in the wind and green beginnings of rain and bending trees

I said   Stop staring at me Mrs Nutt   Theres nothing wrong with me   Go on home and play with Calistra the girl you stole from me   How do you like her anyway have you got your moneys worth

Poor thing said Fanny Knap and Mavis Grant started to move in the door   You know Journal the way women have wanting to come in and feast upon the banquet of suffering   I hit Fanny Knap in the face with your good broad back Journal and I gave Mavis a hard shove   I said   Get out of here what do you know   Ill die before I call you in this house what do you know or care get out and slammed the door

It was only when they scooted away with their laces flying and Mrs Nutt slip sliding about almost falling down on her way out that I realized oh me looking down that I was naked   I looked down saw my nakedness   I held you tight to my old gone bosums Journal and hugged you

Then from the back of the house I heard Taylor calling   She had just come in the back way I thought oh Taylor Taylor

Now Journal you are I think my only hope these days I know I must tell you all and I will only you please do not betray me as I have been somehow somewhere betrayed but not you now please

I heard Taylor calling   She came into the parlour hall from the back of the house   Came in to me there where I stood naked clutching you Journal staring at her saying her name

What in the world said Taylor that wonderful girl and she came running up to me   You are shivering she said

I said   Yes Taylor I am

Well now lets stop that said Taylor   She reached up and pushed my hair back from my face She took my hand   She said   What you need is a quick hot bath and some close covers   Come on now

I said   No Taylor thats not what is needed now dear one and I held her to me as hard as I could sweet Taylor

She stood there patting me on the back as I held her saying now now   Now now

I said   O Taylor sit down just a minute and we sat on my mohair sofa   All the agony then just dipped and vanished Journal into her into Taylor I patted her and she didnt say anything I pulled her dress down and kissed her fine strong shoulder

and got her skirt up and touched her   And then
Journal I captured it again the richness of my
dream all the beauty that goes away when you try
to remember it   The house clean and shining as
a star and the welcome of all my children was in
my grasp as I kissed Taylor and touched her and
moved her until she was still no more but jumping
about on the sofa saying oh oh oh

I said   Yes thats right thats right and like they
all did when they was babies at me long years ago
I bent down there on the sofa and touched my dry
old mouth to her sweet young bosum and O Journal
what a blessing it was

Then Taylor cried and pushed at me and got up

She stood up in the center of the parlour and she
was crying great big tears that little girl   Outside the electrical storm had broken and the green
rain now was pouring and sweeping in through one
of the windows open   By habit I guess Taylor
turned around and closed it carefully crying   She
was saying something to me when she turned around
I didnt hear it at first so blessed was I by the sight
of her body young strong and beautiful

I said what Taylor what honey

Not like those sisters Calistra and Josie was what
she was saying   I said   What what

She said   I have worked for you not because of
that   Not because you are like Mrs Nutt   I
have worked hard and stayed with you because I
liked you very much   I thought you were a good
woman who was in great suffering and I would
learn to bear my own times watching you   I
liked you

I sighed said   Taylor it is all the same   Honey
I am so glad you like me

No no she said   It is not the same   I am
not that way   I dont do that   I like the boys
     You sweet thing I said   I am so glad you do
So did I years ago
     Oh she said and sobbed   Goodbye she said
sobbing and she ran into the back of the house and
in a minute I heard the screen door slam
     So Journal there you are   Taylor has left me
too
     Now I am still alone here   I have not yet put
my clothes on   I sit here writing so hard I have
torn the paper twice and the sweat pours down me
I am sweating from the inside out   I dont mind
I dont know when David will get back   I am
here alone
     Poor Taylor she meant well but when you are
young you dont understand Journal do you
     It seems like the rain and wind now is tearing
the roof off the house   How am I going to do all
the work here alone now all there is to do in this
house   Where am I going to get some help
     O I want me a girl

IV

ANNEALMENT

ANNEALMENT

16   Sabbath   Well I will dress myself as best I can
and I will attend service

17   O Journal Sunday it was something   Today I
got a telegraph from David in the City   He will
be home day after tomorrow   Has lost track he
says of Charlie   Couldnt find him   Says he
will give me details later   Details later Journal
O Charlie little boy I raised to confront me with
whatever it is I may have turned out to be details

later about you I dont know if I want to hear them or not   Still so much speculation I have to get through before David comes home Journal isnt that so   Help me please to think straight I must you know   I have to or I will perish I see that clear enough now my Journal

Let me write about Sunday now   We sat listening to Rev Bayley   He preached away uplifted by the great spirit that filled him but didnt help his asthma none   Hacked and coughed and wheezed his way through all his visions of glory and peace   Gods world is so beautiful he said over and over hacking and wheezing and swallowing you could tell he wanted to be able to lean over that pulpit and spit but couldnt while praising God I heard nothing after awhile   How could I listen to that   I sat thinking that I was turned to stone   That the stone had frozen   And that someone now was breaking up the stone that the pieces of it were my children being broken apart from me cracking splitting and falling away frozen and split   My babies   O darlings when you were born I remember you how misshapped you were heads this way and that faces all twisted and red and ugly little monkeys but alive squawling and warm from my body   O my God to think I would come to this moment sitting before Rev Bayley praising God and his creation but me thinking of them my own darlings frozen stones cracking apart from me   O Journal save me now from this remembrance or let me think it through to the end no matter what that may be it is better I know to perish if that must be than to live now without knowing what it is I have become   Well in

church then listening to Rev Bayley hack and want
to spit and praise God in his witlessness not knowing God created the woman sitting there listening
to him with her babies crumbling away from her
I sobbed a little and felt some better but still
so choked so hard and cold frozen   Then wouldnt
you know I turned my head and I saw William
Craig sitting just behind me in that pew on the
far end   Now I had promised him I would
never accost him his person again but I felt then
that William Craig with his hands bloody forever
with my sweet Alices lost child after all that butch-
ery that mangled spoiled and as the Dictionary
says that wretched performance was my child too
my grandchild the only one I will ever know of
O Jesus in your colored window they say you did
but did you really know such torment   You suffered for us but you did not suffer as a woman not
as a woman now afraid of her own meanness now
suffers   I dont believe you knew anything about
that you were not a woman maybe you were Gods
son but you were not a woman and so what do I
have to do with you now   I took my hymnal
then and my pen I wrote on the first blank page
there under the Sacred Hymnal line I wrote
Hello Wm C   it it seems we are now in this torment
of death together good luck to you I hope you will
wish me the same no matter what else I have said
to you or about you to anyone here signed M E
I just passed the book down to him then signaling
it was to go to him and when he got it I turned to
watch   He got it and read it   It flabbergasted
the man   He gasped and looked down the line
at me but I was standing then with the rest to sing

I sang wondering what will happen when somebody else opens that hymnal reads what I wrote in
it   Will they take it to heart and feel what I
wrote what I meant to be felt   Do others have
happen to them what I wrote to Wm C   I wonder   What will they get out of that Journal do
you suppose
     Well standing then singing Maker of Heaven
& Earth Journal with a dry and cracking voice
singing

> All things bright and beauteous
> All creatures great and small
> All things wise and wondrous
> The Lord God made them all

     Yea standing singing and shivering down to my
heels   I turned looked for some comfort to my
colored window of stained glass knowing the sun
was out and it should be bright   I felt the ache
of Jesuses   no wait wheres the Use of English
All right   I felt the ache where Jesus's lost hand
departed from me   It hurt   I looked and oh
there he was sure enough   In a fine morning
burst of sunlight and stained glass   There again
the beautiful face the torn hands   I whispered
Christ help me   I will stand here and sing my
throat out   I will praise your name forever
Christ I will do anything only put your hand back
again on this shoulder and bear me up over the
dark waters please sir   Just let me know again
that you are there
     He just kept rising   Into the beautiful sky
Eyes turned up to God his father not to me any

more a suffering woman   There was no hand
placed on my shoulder   He kept on going it
seemed to me going up and up and up and the sun-
burst got brighter

I closed my hymn book then   Dropped it on
the seat and left the Church   So busy singing nobody paid me much mind   Singing away all of
them baby sparrows in the nest singing

He gave us eyes to see them
And lips that we might tell
How great is God Almighty
Who made all things well

I admit to some scorn Journal

18 Hard to write burned my hand this morning trying
to make myself some tea   Telegraph from David
he will be home tomorrow   Last night it rained
again a soft long rain I listened to all night
This morning I burned my hand had no breakfast
went out into the yard   Carpet of beautiful grass
so clean and flowers everywhere   Wet and shining   I felt so funny in my own garden and yard
Maybe God had just washed the earth clean like
I used to tell my babies but if so this time he
left me out of it didnt he   I thought O could I
but be like them   Flowers so lovely young and
growing   I would not be gilty then   I even
sat down on the ground among them but could not
touch them and the smell got unbearable for they
are one thing and I am another   Madness Journal to sit like that sprawled on the ground with my
flowers so lovely fashioned so well in the rain and

sun and wind   I dont know what to do about my clothes   No strength to fool with them and since Taylor left they are all dirty   Some of them my dresses all torn at the neck where I pick at them without knowing   Little to wear now yet I cannot be a flower a plant well made a tree even a drop of clear rain though that then was my deepest wish I would be willing then to live just briefly in my season and be gone having done well   My hand hurts so much   Until tomorrow then Journal   There is still a lot to get straight before David comes so much to think over   I will have to study hard in my Dictionary

19 Buttered my hand a lot hasnt helped much   I fear it is enfected infected now but David will be home soon   Anyway I have my Dictionary and my Use of English to help me thats something And you I have you Journal dont I   You will not forsake me and I know about apostrophes now commas too I have studied some

And I cant help it that I am still so confused can I   I must do my best isnt that right   O Charlie where are you now with your angry look What words for your life now and for me   Charlie, when you called me to trial in this house had you been right and it true and me like some poor drunkards she demon had killed them slain my own why it would have been better for me than this You did not know what you were doing to me, you poor boy   But your verdict that you demanded you never got Charlie did you not really   Well, I always tried to give what was needful to my children and you, Charlie, if you are still alive, you

are still my child and I must do that now for you
You have brought me to this and I know I must
do it

What would you say Alice, Ed, Evie   What
would you say to me now and to Charlie   Such
visions I had of all of you but time would not allow
it done   O what would you say what can I ask
from you now   Over your heads I placed what
markers there are to place   Stone towers, black
angels, flowers and evergreen mark your graves and
the hands that placed them there and what good
does any of that do but to strike me now with remembrance of my own gilt and Charlie's angry look
and demand for his verdict which I must now give
to him wherever he is dead or alive but it is yours
too and so I must give it to all of you

So, then, listen here my babies   Did I do this
to you   Or what about this can we say it was
done to all of us together   Can you answer
Journal do you know   Madness to think it but
only the flowers know you see   And if I was only
that I would not worry myself and suffer with you
in this verdict but I am not a flower, Journal, am I
No, not just exactly, am I   Today I passed the
hall mirror with the gilded frame it was Fathers
always hung over his bedroom fireplace   When
I was little I used to go in there stand in front of it
and the firelight would shine on me I would say
help I am touched by King Midus and I am turning
to gold and he would laugh so   Well, today then,
I caught my own eye going past and stopped and
looked   Hair in my face clothes torn and filthy
such a look I gave myself then   No, I am not
flower, am I   But I am what, then   Something

God did not make so well as the gentle flowers harmless in the sun and wind

My darlings, I will believe it has all been done to us   Charlie, you have asked, and son I will give you your verdict now   It is the hardest one though you will not believe it and it is just the same as before not gilty because I did not mean to

20   David has not come today   Am still so confused there is no balm from my own verdict on myself at all I hoped there would be   Cant keep anything on my stomach only tea will do   Inside me such things are happening but what they are I dont know

Same day   Remembered something   About last night when I dreamed again   Much the same, a house, my father, and my children but all so confused   I think it is something else to give up

Same day   I will   I will give that up too   I will worry no more about such things about a day in high heaven when I run to that shining house oh one minute myself a little girl again with my long hair bouncing on my shoulders running up to my father throwing my arms around him turning my face against his vest pressing my ear to his heart Then thats gone   In the next minute myself ancient stately in some shining rainment old and dignified moving as slow and proud as one of Philmon Rudds Corsican women up to the same shining house that has not changed to hold out my arms for my own children running up now to me saying welcome   Something to give up   Such confusion   Yearn no more

Same day   Just now somebody was at the back door   I
went and peeped through my curtains   It was
Calistra   Standing there all alone nothing in her
hands just standing there waiting for the door to
open   Calistra Journal she had come to see me
again   I caught my breath and pulled open the
door and she looked up and saw me and smiled a
little

Well, Calistra, I said, what are you doing here
What will Mrs Nutt say

Calistra made a face then and said never mind
about that   I have come to see you not Mrs Nutt

I thought that I would be angry at her but I was
not   So I said,   Well, in any case it is nice to
see you again   You are looking well   Would
you like to come in and have a cup of tea with me
You will have to make it Im afraid and I held
up my hand   She looked at my hand and at me
and she shook her head and smiled some more

Then she said,   Let me comfort you

I said, O Calistra and she offered her comfort to
me then saying let me help you, poor woman
I am sorry for your suffering and I have been
through some myself you see

What suffering, Calistra, I asked and she just
looked at the ground and said, O Mrs Nutt and
other things just things   Let me comfort you
and myself too, she said   Let me do that

How I ached then   She started to come in but
I said, No, Calistra   I have had done with
comfort now   I have so much else to think about
you see   Your comfort would only slow me down
I would become confused again with pleasure in

this world I have come to live in now   I am sorry
but no
    All right, she said   Whatever you say
    Then I said, But do give me your hand to clasp
    She held out her hand then and I took it and
touched her holding her hand   She smiled at me
then and me at her and we stood holding hands like
two men who have not seen each other in a long
time or who have agreed on something shaking
hands like that and I thought I did not want to let
go of her and I thought then of the last night of each
of my husbands when they left me and my bed and
the leaving and moving into another room away
from me   I held Calistras hand tight   How
good it was then to forgive all the mean and tor-
menting thoughts I have had about her since she
went in with Mrs Nutt   Then Calistra took a
breath and smiled and reached out and patted my
shoulder and it was a good blessing then that last bit
of human comfort I had from her   Human comfort poor women all we are is that
    Thank you for coming, I said
    Any time you want, Calistra said
    No, I said   I have to give you up now and I
do   I have to mean what I say and I do
    She said, All right   Goodbye
    And I said, Calistra, goodbye

Same day   David is home   He gasped to see me forlorn so
very late   dirty my clothes a mess the house a mess
    What has happened to you, woman, he said
    A good deal, David, I said, but never mind about
that now   Tell me the news I have been doing
a lot of thinking and I am ready for it is he dead

Yes I can see you been doing a lot of thinking
David said   Yes I saw Charlie and hes alive
now lets get you taken care of   He wouldnt say
any more Journal until hed taken care of me until
he washed me put me to bed and called Dr Rudge
for my hand   I have a nice thick bandage on
now and so can write without the pen hurting so
When Dr Rudge left David came in with some tea
and sat on the edge of my bed   He was so
calm and his gaze so clear as he told me what he
had to say   He held the saucer for me while I
took the cup in my free hand and sipped and set it
back asking questions and trying to get it clear
and only the little shaking of the saucer there in
his hand gave any sign how David felt

He told me when he got to the City Charlie had
already gone   They told him at the jail that he
had not really done anything so bad just acted too
wild   He had drunk so much he could hardly
stand they say and wouldnt have been put into jail
at all if it had not been a woman there he picked
on   She worked there and called the manager of
the saloon and they started to throw Charlie out so
the policeman told David when Charlie pulled a
knife out and swung it around wildly   The men
got away from him he was so wild and fierce he
scared them with the knife and the wild way he
threatened them and laughed and cursed them
So he held them at bay and began to curse the
woman again saying awful things about her
The men wouldnt get too near him because of the
knife just waiting for the police to come who had
been sent for   But the woman herself finally had
enough of it   She just walked right up to Char-

lie never minding the knife and his wildness and cursing and she slapped him hard in the face

They said Charlie turned white then and they thought he would kill her but he didnt   Drunk and foolish suddenly when she slapped him he coughed turned white dropped his knife on the floor and was sick   The men all laughed then and would have just turned him out thats all but the policeman was there and took Charlie with him because of the knife   In jail at first Charlie went wild again he bit on a chamberpot in his cell until his mouth was bloody and yelled and cried until they told him they would send for a doctor to see if he was crazy or not and Charlie shut up then

When David got there they said theyd let him go that morning and thats all there was to it far as they were concerned because he hadnt hurt any-body really   So Charlie had just vanished then it seemed to David and there was nothing for him to do but come on home

Then when he was ready to get on the train he remembered the boarding house where Charlie lived when he and Ed were working in the City before and the womans name Fay Wilson

He missed his train and went there he said

He rang the doorbell and just as he did one of the boarders and old man with a cane came out of the house and David told me he asked the man if Char-lie was there and the man said yes he thought he was and said go on in

David did and right in the hallway there as he was going in he saw somebody coming down the stairs turning on the landing there and it was Char-lie   He had on a long dressing gown and slippers

and when he saw David he blinked a minute and
David said hello son and Charlie stamped his foot
and started crying like a girl said David shrieking
and yelling until Fay Wilson came and pushed by
him saw David said who are you and what do you
want with him now he didnt hurt anybody

David was very quiet and calm but the saucer
rattled under the teacup   I said quietly well
David what did you say to her

I couldnt hardly hear David he was talking so
low he said   I told her I am his father I have
come to see if he is all right

Then Charlie was crying again David said and
Fay Wilson came down the steps mad   She
pushed David out on the porch and told him never
to come near her place again   Mad hard and
mean said David and I yes I found her out before
when I was there I could see she was a vulgar
woman and I asked David what did he do   He
said he just stood there trying to decide on some
action when he looked up and at one of the windows on the second floor of the boarding house he
saw a face   Charlies   He was staring down
at them crying behind a dirty windowpane and
flopping his hands up and down wringing them
Fay Wilson saw Charlie up there too cursed David
and me too so David said turned went in the house
slammed the door   In a minute David saw her
face in the window too   Her mouth moved like
she was speaking hard and sharp to Charlie who
held out his arms turning away from the window
and somebody drew the shade down then

David I said David

He was sitting there his face twisted and his eyes

staring at nothing but the cup he was holding didnt rattle at all and the saucer was steady   What are you thinking David I said

About all the old people in boarding houses said David who sit and stare at walls all the time and who pull down windowshades

Well I said well see Charlie later when he gets over all this

And David said No I dont think we will and he got up and left holding the saucer carefully so the cup was steady and did not rattle

21   I began to do a little work around the house today I can sweep with one hand and scrub some with one hand   David said oh stop that now and let me get Mr. Hanks in here to help out   I said no   I said we will learn to live with a little dirt until I learn to manage it all myself   I will not have any more help in this house

David shook his head frowned   Then you will run yourself into the ground again he said   With your famous unnecessary work

I said ha David no   I do nothing unnecessary now   He left me alone then

22   In the mail today a letter from the City   Whos this from said David turning the envelope around in his hand wondering without opening it up as if he was scared of it   It turned out to be nothing to do with Charlie   No it was from some men called the Marshall Davis Company and who are in the art market it seems   They were asking about Ed his paintings and about any drawings we might have of his   Isnt that something said

David smiling but I took the letter and crumpled it up and told him I would not have it answered

Why not said David and I said never mind and in the evening David and I cleaned out Eds room and burned the pictures all of them   The big canvas smouldered for a long time there in the back yard by the chickenhouse but it is ashes now   O my babies

23 Sunday   David said why dont you go on to Church you seem strong enough now it might do you good

But what would I sing to David I said and he couldnt understand that and let me alone

What could I sing to now what could I do now there only this put you up there Journal and sing hyms to you just you on the altar all I have now

Same day   Couldnt help myself and just now wrote a letter to Charlie and mailed it   Just a line it said O son how can you hate your own and live in such vile sin   Come back and save yourself my poor boy

O Charlie I would love you even now

24 Today when David came home I had dragged the hall carpet out into the yard got it up on the wire with my good hand and was beating it   David stood and watched me and said what are you doing to yourself

Nothing I said I am just beating the dust out of my carpet here what do you mean

He said well you act like you have put yourself in a carpenters clamp and you yourself are turning

it tighter and tighter   Its beginning to hurt me
too   Let loose

If I did that David I would die tomorrow I said
Allow me this, my new vision of the world, please
sir

What new vision of the world are you talking
about he said

I beat the carpet and the dust flew out and I
was grimy but didnt care David asked me again
what vision and I said the one I have now   A
world I see that is as flat and hard as the face of
my clothes iron   A world I said that is that way
and this way too and I hit the carpet with all my
might

David left me alone then

25 For the first time Journal in my life I have been
worrying about David and how he is   Yesterday
he brought in the carpet from the wire outside when
I had finished with it   Bringing it in the door he
dropped it picked it up too quick and sprained his
back   By today it was wrenched into a tight fix
and so I rubbed him with linament just a little
while ago

As I did that working over his back, he had his
chin in his hands sitting on the edge of his bed
there   I rubbed and once he said, Ouch   He
said, ouch, and looked around uneasy   I rubbed
and then David drew a breath and a whistle and
said owy again and then looked at me darkly saying quick, Not so hard please dont kill me too

I fell back away from him then and cried out,
David David how could you say that

He said, Im sorry   Im sorry you know I didnt
mean that like it sounded

O you did I said   You did   And he did not
answer me   I watched him sit there with his shirt
off his galluses down hanging off his trousers sitting
with his chin still in his hands looking at me darkly
still saying Im sorry with no conviction to it
   I dried the linament off my hands with a rag
I said, David you are thinking of leaving me arent
you   Must I loose you too
   David took his chin out of his hands then and
he scratched his head   He looked funny and foolish but was not and I worried about him   Until
this minute it was like David never had a part in
what had happened and now he did   I waited
and held my breath
   He scratched and rubbed his face and then he
said,   No, I am not going to leave you not if you
dont want me to   Youre my wife   We can live
here together just as it has been   Only there is
one thing I have to say and get straight and I guess
it better be done now
   I said, What is that and waited
   David said,   You will have to remember this and
keep it in your mind at all times   I have spent
the last of our savings on my trip to the City and
on Eds funeral   I have sold my interest in the
other store in Dansville   Not much is left now
So if anything happened to me you would be out of
luck   You would have to go and run that store
yourself and all by yourself
   I said,   David what terrible thing are you trying to say to me your own wife
   He said, Oh you heard me   What do you
think about it
   I think it is awful the way you have put it, I said
It does me little honor

Well never mind about that, he said, do you understand me or dont you

He was not looking darkly then but calmly and his eyes clear decided and a little stern and ready for me to say whatever it was I was going to say Firm he was   I thought O David and I started to say what a fool he was acting but I didnt   He meant for me to answer and I saw that and regarded David anew a little and thought then I could stop worrying about him

I said, I understand you, David, and for your information, I dont even mind what you have said

All right, then, he said   Thanks for rubbing my back in that case   Then slowly and carefully he got his shirt back up and he even tried to smile at me while he slipped his galluses back over his shoulders, got up and left the room to go on back to the store

He has his dignity, David   Even if nobody in the world but me sees it   And I cant imagine David dead Journal can you

26   When I was a little girl there were times when I would be in the City Journal   Some of those times my father would take me to walk in the great City Park   One time something had just been put up in the center of a fountain   It was a tall high thing of some kind reaching up way high and it was very slender   What it was actually I dont remember or where it was even or where it stands now but I do remember being there holding Fathers hand   It was winter and there was some snow and a lot of wind was blowing   There was all sorts of things holding the monument up propping

it, there were scaffolds and butresses of wood and all of that   When we came by they were taking them all away   When they took the last of them away there was a hushed minute when the workmen and all of us standing there wondered if the thing would stand   It did   They moved the supports away and it stood   But what pain

27 Mrs Phiney came by to see me today   We talked two or three minutes   Looked at me sideways waiting for me to confide something in her   I wouldnt do it   They have started testimonials at the Temperence meetings   Souls are being saved she said   I almost laughed out loud and she saw that and left   But she did smile at me once or twice and when she left she was nice A silly woman but it was good of her to come Journal   Journal how hard it is alone   I have learned about apostrophes havent you see haven't I But I forget   Wouldnt do it is wouldn't do it

28 This monument is still standing Journal   I owe it to you all to you   How wonderful it has been having you to hold me up as I have gone over these dark waters   I love you so much   You have been a better friend than Jesus   Yes this monument is swaying but still standing   Will it fall I don't know   And what after all is it a monument of   Answer me that Journal answer me that

Same day   I just got a postcard from Charlie answering my letter   All it said was   Dear Mother this vile sin my salvation at least Im alive Charlie

O my boy   You never had much backbone
did you

29   Am quite sick   Have a terrible headache I feel
I am going to split   A horrible sight today Journal   I went out on the porch and looked down
the street and there on their porch the Hardy Allens
Do you know she is still alive Mrs Hardy Al-
len's mother   Out there soaking up the sun still
alive   She should have died years ago but she
won't   And my babies are gone   I watched her
out there eating a bowl of soup way over ninety
years old   Alive by whose hand Journal as mine
are gone by whose hand Journal   I watched her
in the sun alive and ran for my Dictionary thinking
I had the word   Remorseless that is the word
It fits my new vision   So sick I am now and
weak, I have been here on the sofa almost all day
Feel as though I am sinking and falling   My head
is about to split and my heart pounds so   Life or
death just lying here on this mohair sofa life or
death Journal which   I cant care any more I can't

30   Sunday   After making breakfast for me David
laid out a dress he took off to someone to clean and
press   Laid it out with my parasol but I said No
He said, Oh go ahead, a nice walk to Church and
back will do you good   I said, No, but I will put
on the dress since you have gone to the trouble to
have it cleaned and mended for me
    My head still hurt and my heart pounded but
David was right it did feel good to wear the dress
and I even twirled the parasol once in my hands
Then I thought well, I will take a walk, why not,

I don't have to hide, no matter what happens to me
do I   I said, Thank you, David, I might take
a short walk but I will wait until noon and Church
is over

So then I went into the back of the house to have
tea and rest and write to you Journal   Poor
David how can he know maybe I will live to take
this walk and maybe I will not   My head I wish
it would go ahead and split   My heart I wish it
would go on and leap out of this body

Same day   Something has happened to me Journal   Something definite   I feel I will be able to tell you
about it calmly now

I walked down to the stores at noon   I did not
know then if I would ever come home again and I
did not care   A few people here and there I paid
no notice just faces and passings and buzzings
I passed the Church   It was after the service but
there were some people there   At my elbows suddenly were Mavis Grant and Mrs Phiney   They
had come up to me and were talking to me   I
didn't know what they were saying and I said,
What, what, isn't the service over by now, I thought
it would be

They said, Yes, it is but didn't you know, Carrie Wheaton's baby is going to be christened
Come in with us, come in   No, I said, No, I
don't feel like it but I could not make them understand and so allowed myself to be taken by them
into the Church in their insistence holding me by
the arms both of them

How strange it was   The Church, it seemed to
me like a depot station or a courtroom   I don't

remember who was there and who wasn't but it was almost full   I stayed just because Mavis and Mrs Phiney were too much for me and I could not argue but I had great misgivings there and was almost crying from my headache and found that I was picking at my dress again tearing it again where David had it mended   Then I think I did begin to cough and felt choked, that I was to fall then, and in a great panic I looked about to find a way to get out of there

But then Carrie Wheaton and her husband came walking down the aisle bringing their baby to Rev Bayley   Someone I think maybe it was Elaine Ruskin was singing a hymn solo that now in calmness I think was out of place   At that time all I wanted was outside air to get out of that place but I heard the baby then being carried down to Rev Bayley   It hooed and booed and cried being handed to Rev Bayley but he rocked it a little and hushed it up and it only whimpered some and I listened to that and stayed where I was

Carrie Wheaton, now let me see   Yes, married April 15 only one year ago   Just after I started keeping you, Journal   And now she already has this baby her first   O   Well, she stood there watching her child being given up to Rev Bayley, put into his arms and I began to shiver then
I felt that I could not breathe and that I was choking

Then the christening was about to occur   My chest burned and my hands sweated but I felt so cold in spite of that and my heart began to beat even faster   There was a quick tiny little wail from that baby as Rev Bayley held it up too jerky or something and I thought then it is over and I am going to die here now   But I felt something begin inside me   It was a slow and deep shock It was something painful and yet thrilling and I felt it up and down my body from my head to my toes

And I remembered Journal then like a vision Charlie Robinson in his blacksmith shop working and firing and pounding the metal until it glowed white hot in the pinchers then holding it up quick and quick with a sudden thrust plunging it down into his great rainbarrel of dark water and the fierce hiss and boiling clouds of steam that rose up then   He took the metal out and held it up in the pinchers   Do you know what that was, he asked me once when I stood there watching him a curious little girl   And I said, No, sir And he said, That was annealment It will not change now   It is tempered and it is tough

Oh, I said,   Is that right

Then I saw the holy water fall from Rev Bayley's hand and I wondered that it did not hiss, steam, and rise scaulding from that child's head I raged, thinking how we are used   Baptised into one new life when we are young   Annealed into another when we are old and it has finished with us   O little baby Wheaton, I thought, and I fought all my feelings

It was over then and the baby began to hoo and boo again   My rage and my shaking spell went away and my hands stopped sweating, my heart became calm and my head seemed clear   Mavis and Mrs Phiney looked at me   I looked back and them and smiled and they smiled

I stood there like the gourd whose seeds are cut away   Like Philemon Rudd's Corsican woman alone by the sea in a flapping black dress

July 1   There is to be a Temperence meeting tonight I have decided that I will go   Mavis is coming by the house to go there with me   I had some trouble dressing myself right because of my hand and David helped me   He said, You look right as rain, old girl   Right as rain, he would say that David   You go ahead, old girl, and let them know about things   You go tell them what's what Oh, David, I said, such a fool you are but I smiled and I came in here to go to Temperence with Mavis, writing now while I wait

Same day   Well, I was very shaky, Journal, but got through the meeting all right   A new thing they do now is this, they have these testimonials   Tonight it was Maurice Kelp, a man who has been a drunkard in this town for years and years but because he worked in the state government office here, he always got away with it   Well, he got up tonight and told of the awful life he has lived   Of the terrible waste and misguided times   Of course everyone urged him on, eager for the salvation of his besotted soul   It was lively, I will say that for it   And of course, it is a blow against the town councils having a government man like Maurice Kelp testify

But aside from that, much the same a whole lot of confusion with Mrs Nutt lording over all When Mavis came in bringing me with her Mrs Nutt glared and looked away quick   Then after the Kelp testimonial Mrs Nutt choosing who would speak and who wouldn't, cutting people off and ruling with her iron hand   And they still haven't got the right name yet   They had a lot of talk going nowhere   I held up my hand to say something but Mrs Nutt wouldn't point to me   Finally Mavis held up her hand and when Mrs Nutt pointed to her she turned to me and said,   Go ahead now   Say what you please

So I stood up and said,   Well, how about my slogan that I put forth a while ago here   Has that been decided on or not

Mrs Nutt was furious, you could see she thought she had been tricked into letting me talk by Mavis I suppose Calistra has nothing to do with her now and she may think I am the reason   Let her think what she pleases   Anyway she glared at me while the others remembered my slogan and there was a murmur of approval

Then Mrs Nutt said,   We have it under advisement

I said,   Yes, I knew it was under something

I sat down again but I felt another shock Journal, a small one this time but quite noticable   I jumped up, never minding Mrs Nutt's pointing or anything and I said,   Wait   I have it I know the name

There was a busy murmur and Mrs Nutt glared and looked like she was biting a lemon, but she had to nod to me and say, Well, what is it

And I felt better than I have felt in such a long time   I said, It is this   Band of Hope That's what we must call it   Band of Hope

Right, cried out Maurice Kelp in a great voice

He can be a very emotional man   He wept, crying that was right   The perfect name   There was applause then   Everybody likes it fine except Mrs Nutt

2   Mavis Grant   Mrs Phiney   Fanny Knap young Elaine Ruskin and even a few others came to see me just now   They wanted to talk about the Temperence movement and we did, sitting on my porch   It tired me out a lot   There was a minute there when I thought, oh, I am too tired for this   And I thought, what am I doing anyway This is all so silly this is not my vision but then someone would ask me something and I would have to listen to reply and so the afternoon went on I got so tired and was about to tell them I had to stop when Mrs Nutt came walking down the street I spoke to her nicely and asked her to join us but she shook her head and looked at us all darkly, like she was counting the noses of those who were there with me   Then she marched on without a word   Insulting to all of us and the ladies all felt it   I said, Well, that's just Mrs Nutt for you   More nerve than a bad tooth   And they all laughed   I sat down again and was able to keep on with them for some time and felt so good I was able to spend the rest of the day washing out a few clothes as well as I can   Tonight I am going to devote myself to hard study   I owe it to these Temperence people I think

3   Yesterday I was working on Correct English Usage and this idea came to me. I am composing a hymn, Journal. I have the first verse and I even

touched out a kind of tune on the piano. This is the first verse, see what you think about it Journal

> Arise, my sleeping, tender soul, arise
> Pour torrents from my melting eyes.
> And you my heart, in anguish beat,
> While any drunkard perish in the street.

When I am finished, we will see what they say about it at the Temperence meeting. Look out, Mrs Nutt, you can't lord it over everybody. We each have our talents.

4   Well, I must say again, it was some fourth of July.

People here in town have long thought that the parade through the town ought to have more fancy to it some way or other. So there was a great costume parade. The idea was to see whose would be the best, in individual prize and in a group prize, and the way they went about it was to take all the children and the youngsters up to sixteen years, and dress them all up in fancy costumes and parade them in a long line behind the Mayor's wagon past a judge's stand. Individuals wore funny faces, masks, and such, and the groups were all dressed just alike. The first prize went to Jimmy Toller, who was dressed as Uncle Sam, second prize to Robert Sales, dressed as Moses. There was only one prize in the group award and it went to Elaine Ruskin's Sunday School Choir, twenty-six pretty little girls and boys all dressed in white. Of course the youngsters didn't take the parade very seriously, yet it was fun to watch them, even when they would cut up a little. I had to laugh and feel joyful about them in spite of myself.

The fire companies got together again and there was a great deal of fireworks and explosions, though nothing out at Keith River this time. It was happily a beautiful and clear day. The first thing the town heard this morning was the sound of the guns and the band playing. So much to make us laugh and be gay.

There was, however, only one thing to bring on any dishonor. During the military citizen's march, I saw it and I protested. It was the Brewery Companies who were out in full force, over thirty large teams loaded with barrels and casks to show the immense trade they have in manufacturing Ale and Beer. I felt it was a disgrace to this good old state, so I raised my voice to them as they passed, saying, Go home, go home, shame on you for this sinful display you have made. Many Temperence people then joined me in taking a stand, and we did manage to make ourselves heard.

Then there was the picnic, just at the edge of town this time. I felt light hearted, Journal, and I went to Elaine Ruskin's group of little girls and boys. They were all dressed in white. Such beautiful children, the sight of them in such pure finery, it dazzled me. One little girl asked me who I was, and I told her, and she said, Pleased to meet you, and held out her little hand. I took it and shook hands with her, and then the next thing I knew I had the child in my arms and was hugging her and fussing over her so that David came quick to get me. He led me away from all those beautiful children in white and told me to calm myself. I managed to do that, and soon found company with the ladies and we talked about our next meeting.

It was a big day, one like it we shall surely never see again. The people were all orderly and when night came on we were all glad to go home and rest.

5   Temperence meeting tonight. Rev Bayley was present to preach to us. But first, I read them my hymn, and Elaine Ruskin sang the tune. Much approval, Journal. Fanny Knap came over and hugged me around the shoulders and Mavis Grant made an immediate motion to adopt my slogan about King Alcohol. Mrs Nutt did the best she could to swamp it under a lot of fast talk but it got through the vote. Then Mavis looked around at everyone and said in a loud voice, Listen here, why not Band of Hope as our name, I for one think it is fine. But Mrs Nutt like a tiger jumped on her and said that we couldn't consider that now, as Rev Bayley was here to preach to us, and she gave the floor then to Rev Bayley and shut Mavis up.

Rev Bayley then preached and at the end he said before we start any further on our program that we must take this time to examine ourselves anew. We must be sure, he said, that there is no taint in ourselves before we go forth in our program for others. We all considered that, and pondered it. He prayed, we sang, and then he asked for sinners among us to come forth and testify, and accept forgiveness, in the name of the Lord.

What can I say, Journal, except that I saw my moment and took it, that I took action then. By all rights I think I might despise myself, but I do not, and there you have it, Journal. I stood up and though I felt very strange taking this move, and thought for a minute I was doing something even more wretched than anything before, still I stood up and walked to Rev Bayley and knelt down before him. There were gasps of Oh No, and much consternation among the public gathered there, and great pity for me as I faced the crowd and confessed that I have been a bad woman. There were cries of hush, and no, they all shook their heads and murmured no, no, with all she has been through, no, she shouldn't be up there but I was. I told them that I have done much wrong, but got no further than that, because Mavis called out, No, no you have not, and Mrs Phiney was weeping openly. I stared over them at Mrs Nutt, who was furious and biting at her lip but who could say nothing and who finally had to force a smile and a gracious nod, and so my purpose it was then accomplished, I could feel it.

Now, Journal, we have been together for quite a while, haven't we? I have learned from you a lot, that is so true. And it has been you who held me up when I was failing, yes, that's right. Without you, I would not be here at all, I feel. I would be under the dark waters, but you have helped me cross them. Yet the time has come to part, I'm afraid. Going back over it all, reading again what has happened to me, I think it is best to say goodbye now. I do not really understand it all very well, and indeed, I do not want to because it still frightens me, though I am now so much better in mind and body. I love you, Journal, more than I can ever say, but there is really not the need for this any more, is there? So, when I have finished this entry, I am going to take you into the back yard and burn you where no one will ever see you, in the back yard where Ed's painting and drawings were burned, where Alice and Evie and my poor bold Charlie each in their turn played games there by the chicken-house at one time or other. Also, I will put in with you my Dictionary and Mr. Moorehead's Correct English Usage because I have learned enough about all that now. Also, I will put in Philemon Rudd's travel book with Ed's last picture in it, the picture of Jesus, and the tales of the Corsican women. I do not need to read about them any more. I know about them without the book, the Corsican women.

But first, before I do this, I will finish this entry, and make all balance out. I have learned to be neat, and you have taught me, so I owe you a finished entry, dear Journal.

It seems that when I sat back down after going up to confess myself such a sinner unworthy of the great work of Christian Temperence, Mrs. Phiney would not stop crying, and Mavis began to cry, and Fanny Knap with her face all flushed, waving her arms, got up and said she didn't care how a person should or should not do it, but that she was putting me in immediate nomination for Lady Superintend-ant of the Band of Hope. There was a great cry from all present. Mrs. Nutt couldn't say a word. Rev Bayley nodded and smiled, too.

I told them how overwhelmed I was, and that I could not speak now, but wanted to leave to think the challenge of such a possible thing over very carefully. They stood back and let me pass, all silent. When I was at the door, someone said, Noth-ing more will be done until she decides. And as I walked down the street, they came out of the building, the meeting broken up, and they watched me walk along, thinking deeply.

I walked for awhile, considering this possible new life, and the duties it might hold. I found myself passing the Cemetary, with all the monuments there of what it has claimed from me, all that I have given up worrying about now. I was passing it by when out of a dark shadow there by the gate stepped Mrs. Nutt, and stood in my path. Her eyes were swollen and her face was dark. She was leaning on her umbrella to hold herself up, I think. She glared at me, in great misery, but she held forth her hand and took mine.

"You have won," said Mrs. Nutt. I said nothing but passed her by.

So it seems that I will be elected, though I thought it would be someone else. God help me for I am very weak and can do nothing of myself.

I only hope that I may do some good among the youth.

Goodbye, Journal.